SUBMARINES
of the 20TH
CENTURY

SUBMARINES
of the 20TH
CENTURY

Christopher Chant

Illustrated by John Batchelor

TIGER BOOKS INTERNATIONAL
LONDON

This edition published in 1996 by
Tiger Books International PLC, Twickenham
© Graham Beehag Books, Christchurch, Dorset
All rights reserved
Printed and bound in Singapore

ISBN 1-85501-804-7

Contents

Introduction

T HE submarine is a vessel designed and built to operate under the surface of the sea so that it can avoid the comparatively easy detection that is the fate of vessels operating on the surface of the sea: this 'cloak of invisibility' has the twin advantages of allowing the undetected submarine to avoid the easy interception that can swiftly lead to destruction, and to 'sneak up' on the enemy and inflict a telling blow before this enemy has been able to undertake anything in the way of evasive manoeuvres and/or defensive measures. This cloak of invisibility has long been a desire of armed forces, and the notion of a submarine vessel therefore had great attraction from early times. There were almost certainly designs (if not prototypes) in the period up to the end of the sixteenth century, but no known records of these efforts survive.

In the years between 1575 and 1765 many submarines were designed, and the designs of at least 17 survive today. The four men who made the greatest strides in this difficult field were the Englishman William Bourne, the Dutchman Cornelius van Drebbel, and the Americans David Bushnell and Robert Fulton. It was the two Americans who made the most notable contributions.

Bushnell was born in 1742 and graduated from Yale in 1775, just before the beginning of the War of Independence (1776-83). Bushnell was bitter in his opposition to the British, and designed a small 'submarine' as the means whereby the Americans, who lacked any form of effective navy, might be able to attack the fleet on which the British relied for the shipment of men, matériel and supplies from England, and also for transport and tactical mobility along the eastern litoral of the North American continent. Bushnell's *Turtle* was shaped like an egg, and by the flooding of two small internal tanks it could be trimmed right down in the water so that its conning tower was awash. Propulsion was provided by a hand-cranked propeller, and offensive capability rested with a 150lb charge of gunpowder that was designed to be attached to the

With hand-powered propellers for horizontal and vertical propulsion and snorkel-type tubes for the admission of breathing air, the *Turtle* designed by David Bushnell was the first 'practical' submarine in history, and was in fact a semi-submersible that could be trimmed right down into the water for concealed attacks with the 150lb (58kg) black powder charge contained in the hollowed-out oak container carried on the back of the vehicle and designed to be attached to the target by a screw. The boat was used operationally on at least one occasion in September 1776, but was defeated on its attack on a British battleship by the thick copper plating used to prevent infestation of the lower hull by shipworm.

underside of the target ship by a screw. In 1776, the Bushnell 'submarine' was launched against the British fleet lying off New York: manned by Sergeant Ezra Lee, the 'submarine' reached the *Eagle*, flagship of Admiral Lord Howe, but could not deposit its charge as Bushnell had forgotten that British warships were plated with copper that resisted the penetration of the screw. Two other unsuccessful efforts were made later in the war, but in 1782 Bushnell gave up his efforts and became a doctor.

Fulton was born in 1765 and, after an early working life as a jeweller's apprentice and portrait painter, decided that engineering should be his career. In 1794, he travelled to England and became involved in canal engineering, but, in 1797, he moved to France and turned his attention to an uphill struggle to persuade the French that they needed submarines to defeat the British at sea. In 1801, Fulton managed to persuade Napoleon of his concept's validity and received 10,000 francs to design and build a prototype, the *Nautilus*. The submarine was ellipsoid in shape, 21ft (6.40m) long and 7ft (2.13m) in maximum diameter, and could be submerged by opening cocks to flood internal tanks. Surface propulsion was provided by a collapsible mast and sail, and underwater propulsion by hand-cranked propeller. A first test in Brest was successful when the *Nautilus* placed an external charge under a schooner anchored in the harbour, but the French marine ministry remained sceptical. Fulton then tried his luck in Britain with equal lack of success, and then returned to the USA, where his concept was also turned down. In 1812, Fulton devised his 'turtle-boat', a semi-submersible for operations against the British in the War of 1812: this boat was propelled by a hand-cranked propeller and designed to flood down to a freeboard of only 6in (0.15m) so that the craft could, at night, be mistaken for a floating log. The 'weapon' carried by the turtle-boat was a series of towed floating charges which could be swung against the target vessel and detonated from a safe distance with a lanyard. The first trial was not successful, and the turtle-boat was then destroyed by a British raiding party before further trials could be undertaken. Fulton went on to make his name as a pioneer of steam power for ships.

The semi-submersible was also used in the American Civil War (1861-65). The type used by the Confederate navy carried the name 'David'. The 'Davids', of which some 20 were built, were intended to redress the considerable numerical superiority of the Union navy and came in two basic forms, using steam or hand power. The best known exploit of a steam-powered 'David' was the attack on the Federal ship *New Ironsides* in Charleston harbour in October 1863: under the command of Lieutenant Glassel, the 'David' did not get its spar torpedo (a 132lb/60kg explosive charge at the end of a long pole) deep enough under the water before the charge was exploded by its impact fuses, and the resulting waves swamped and sank the 'David' without causing more than limited damage to its target. More success attended a hand-propelled 'David', the *H.L. Hunley*, committed against the Federal ship *Housatonic* just as she was about to set sail in February 1864: the *Housatonic* was holed and opened to the sea. She sank, taking down with her the successful 'David', whose crew of nine was found inside the sunken vessel when divers went down to the wrecks some years later.

A successful submarine clearly depended on a number of primary requirements: a hull of circular section to withstand water pressure when

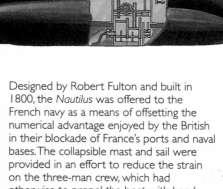

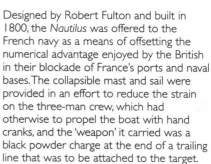

Designed by Robert Fulton and built in 1800, the *Nautilus* was offered to the French navy as a means of offsetting the numerical advantage enjoyed by the British in their blockade of France's ports and naval bases. The collapsible mast and sail were provided in an effort to reduce the strain on the three-man crew, which had otherwise to propel the boat with hand cranks, and the 'weapon' it carried was a black powder charge at the end of a trailing line that was to be attached to the target.

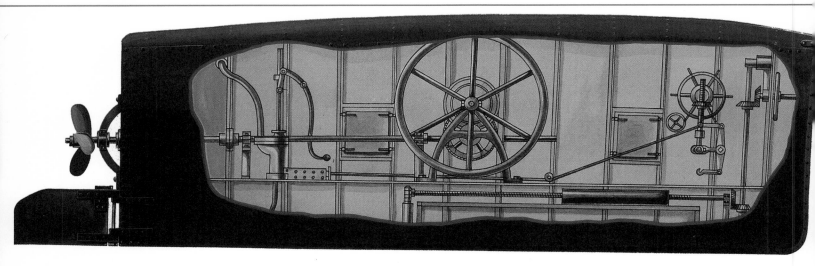

submerged, ballast tanks that could be filled with water to make the submarine sink and then refilled with air to restore the buoyancy to bring the boat back to the surface once more, a powerplant able to function without a constantly replenished supply of air when the submarine was submerged, a rudder to provide directional control, and horizontal rudders (hydroplanes) to provide longitudinal control. The hydroplanes also needed to be controllable either collectively so that, for example, a positive angle on both planes would bring the submarine upwards without changing its longitudinal angle, or differentially for a bow-up or bow-down angle to speed surfacing or submerging respectively.

The development of metal construction (initially iron and later steel) opened the possibility of ships and also of submarines with a watertight hull of considerable strength without excessive thickness and, during the second half of the nineteenth century, American and French inventors developed a number of designs up to model form. None of them secured the official backing that could have turned them into full-size hardware. This was perhaps just as well, for the major problems yet to be overcome were underwater propulsion and an effective underwater weapon. Steam power could be used for surface propulsion, of course, but was impractical because of the time needed to damp down the boilers before submerging and to get up a head of steam after surfacing. The practical solution appeared in 1885 with the invention of the internal-combustion engine by Gottlieb Daimler: some years had to elapse before it had been made powerful and reliable enough to use on board ships, but it offered the possibility of instant shut-down and start-up. However, such an engine cannot be used under water, since it needs a

The *Plongeur Marin was* designed during 1850 by the Bavarian Wilhelm Bauer, and its propulsive momentum was provided by the iron weight that could be moved fore and aft to plane forward in a series of undulating dives and climbs. The threat of the boat, built at Kiel, was sufficient to keep the Danish navy at a respectful distance from Kiel in the Prusso-Danish dispute over Schleswig-Holstein until the boat sank in February 1851 after a structural failure. Bauer and his two crew members became the first to survive a submarine accident.

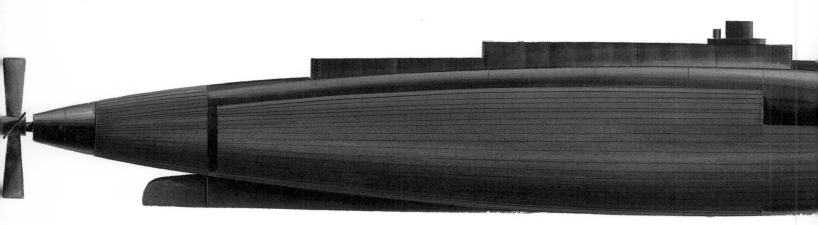

supply of air so large that the engine would exhaust the submarine's supply of compressed breathing and ballast-blowing air in a very short time.

For underwater running, a combination of electric engines and a massive array of batteries provided one solution. This combination had its limitations, however. Surface running could be entrusted to the internal-combustion engine, which could also be used to charge the batteries of the underwater system. The main drawback to the idea was the need for the submarine to surface periodically to recharge the batteries, but this problem could be reduced by surfacing at night or in safe conditions. This means, though, that the submarine with combined internal-combustion and electrical propulsion should perhaps be thought of as a submersible rather than as a true submarine as the type cannot be genuinely independent of the surface.

The right weapon was found in the locomotive torpedo, a free-running weapon developed into an effective type by Robert Whitehead, a British engineer working at Fiume in Austria-Hungary. The torpedo used compressed air for motive power and had a hydrostatic valve (later a pendulum system) for stability of depth. The first trials were undertaken in 1867, and by 1869 the locomotive torpedo was a practical weapon that was rapidly adopted by most of the world's more advanced navies. The type was still limited, but progress was made steadily in improving the torpedo's range, speed and course-keeping, the last with the aid of a gyroscopic system invented in Trieste by L. Obry in 1881. The first production torpedo emerged for the Royal Laboratory at Woolwich, England, in the early 1870s: it was a 16in (406mm) weapon with contra-rotating propellers (in which the torque reaction of each unit cancelled that of the other and therefore removed the tendency of single-propeller torpedoes to roll and thus change course in the direction of the roll), for a range of 1,000 yards (915m) at 7 knots or 300 yards (275m) at 12.5 knots. The pace of development is indicated by the fact that in 1909 the standard Whitehead torpedo was an 18in (457mm) weapon with a range of 2,000 yards (1830m) at 35 knots or 4,000 yards (3660m) at 29 knots. Further development was in the pipeline through the enrichment of the torpedo's air oxidant: the British developed a steam/gas engine in which water was evaporated and superheated by a shale-oil jet, while the Americans produced the Bliss-Leavitt type with a turbine driven by steam heated by an alcohol torch.

Lacking the resources to match the large fleets that the Union was able to create in the American Civil War (1861-65), the Confederacy opted for a 'high-technology' response to its opponent's surface warships. This was the combination of the spar torpedo (a large explosive charge at the end of a wooden spar extended over the bow) and the submarine, and given their planned task of killing the Union 'giants', these boats received the generic name 'Davids'. The first such boat was the *David*, funded by Theodore Stoney and built at Charleston, South Carolina, before being presented to the Confederate navy. The boat was constructed largely of boiler plate, and was based on a cylindrical central section with conical fore and after ends. A small boiler in the forward part of the boat generated the steam that powered the single engine powering the four-blade propeller at the extreme stern. Being unable to submerge completely, the *David* was not a true submarine but rather a semi-submersible: water was allowed to flood ballast tanks that trimmed the boat down into the water so that only some 10ft (3.05m) of the superstructure, including the hatch and the cylindrical funnel, were awash and could, it was hoped, be mistaken for a floating log or other such natural phenomenon. The *David* was 54ft (16.45m) long and was armed with a spar torpedo extending from the bow: this was designed to be lowered below the surface so that the detonation of its 134lb (60.8kg) of gunpowder, under the influence of seven chemical impact fuses, would blow a large hole in the side of the target below the waterline. The dangers of such a boat even under non-operational conditions were revealed when it was swamped and sunk by the wash of a ship during its trials, but the boat was raised and readied for action. In October 1863 the *David*, with a volunteer crew under the command of Lieutenant Glassell, attacked the broadside ironclad New Ironsides. The *David* was seen and challenged by the watch of the Union warship, but the Union sailors were disconcerted by a volley of rifle fire from the *David*'s hatch, which killed one Union officer and provided enough time for the spar torpedo to hit the ship abreast the engine room. The resulting explosion was too near the waterline to cause fatal damage, but sprang the wooden side of the ship for some 4 to 5in (0.10 to 0.127m) over a length of 50ft (15.25m). The explosion also swamped the *David*, putting out the boiler fire and washing Glassell overboard. Glassell and two other members of the crew swam to safety.

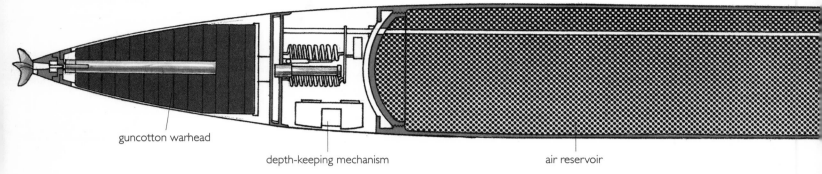

guncotton warhead

depth-keeping mechanism

air reservoir

By 1914, torpedoes were generally of 18 or 21in (457 or 533mm) diameter, with lengths of 17.5 and 22ft (5.33 and 6.71m) respectively and ranges of 3,750 yards (3,430m) at 44 knots or 10,000 yards (9,145m) at 28 knots.

The torpedo was thus the ideal weapon for the submarine: it was designed to run underwater in any case, and in submarines it could be launched by either of two methods: in the drop-collar method the torpedoes were carried externally and merely released from their mountings, and in the tube-launched method the torpedoes were fired by compressed air out of flooded tubes that could then be purged of water by the closing of the bow doors and reloaded from inside the submarine if the vessel was large enough to carry a reserve supply. The latter method fairly rapidly became the norm as it offered lower drag and therefore higher underwater speed, and allowed the withdrawal of the torpedo from its tube for limited maintenance if required.

These features all combined in the fertile mind of an Irish-born American, John P. Holland, who may be regarded as the father of the true submarine. The first Holland submarine was the *Plunger,* a design commissioned by the US Navy and built by the Columbian Iron Works in 1896. Because of the naval requirements the design was too complex for its small size, and the *Plunger* was not successful. The contract was cancelled in 1900, the year in which the US Navy bought the sole example of Holland's next design, which had been designed as a private venture and built by Crescent. This seven-man vessel had surfaced and submerged displacements of 64 and 74 tons on a length of 53.75ft (16.38m), and with 50hp (37.3kW) available from its gasoline or electric

The device that was eventually to make the submarine a viable weapon of war was the Whitehead locomotive torpedo, seen here in its first effective form of 1868. From nose to tail, the primary features are the guncotton warhead with impact fuse, the depth-keeping mechanism, the compressed air reservoir, the compressed air motor, and the tail section with its rudders and contra-rotating propeller unit.

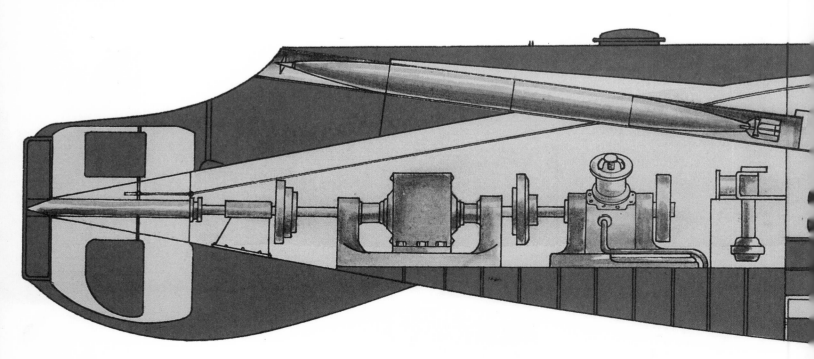

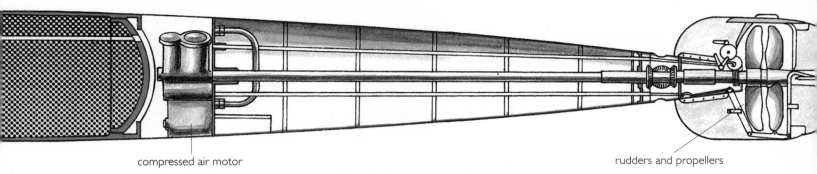

compressed air motor   rudders and propellers

engines had surfaced and submerged speeds of 8 and 5 knots respectively. The armament included one 18 in (457mm) torpedo tube and one 8in (203mm) dynamite gun. The concept clearly held promise, and there followed a group of seven 'A' class submarines which were slightly larger and provided improved underwater performance.

Several other countries began to develop submarines around the turn of the century. Germany was an exception, as its navy preferred to wait for the perfection of the considerably safer and more economical compression (rather than spark) ignition engine invented by Diesel and which ran on comparatively heavy oil instead of volatile gasoline, which made for considerably greater safety in the confined spaces inside a submarine and which, incidentally, offered much superior fuel economy. This last factor gradually came to assume a significant importance as the greater range possible, on a given volume of fuel, allowed the development of the diesel-engined boat as an independent long-range weapon for commerce raiding rather than a subordinate medium-range weapon associated with battle fleet evolutions on the surface.

The first diesel-engined submarine was the French *Aigrette*, which was launched in January 1904, and this was followed in 1906, 1910 and 1911 by the Russian *Minoga*, British D2 and American *Skipjack*.

The first submarine design by John Holland, arguably the true 'father' of the submarine, was the *Plunger* ordered by the US Navy in 1895 but never accepted by the US Navy as the type was an unsuccessful effort to fit too much capability into a design limited in size by the navy's lack of resources and then constantly altered during the course of construction in the light of changing naval opinions.

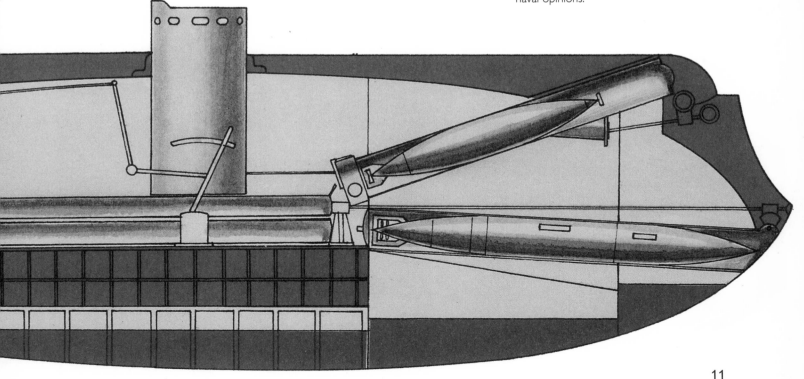

11

The Submarine in World War I

THE first German *Unterseeboot* (underwater boat, otherwise submarine) was the U1 that appeared in 1906 as a 19-man vessel that was 139ft (42.37m) long. At surfaced and underwater displacements of 238 and 283 tons, it was capable of 10.7 and 7 knots respectively on its gasoline or electric motors, each developing 400hp. The armament was still limited, made up of just one 17.7in (450mm) torpedo tube. This was a 'traditional' boat with the generally unsuccessful combination of a gasoline engine for surfaced running and battery charging, and an electric motor for submerged running. The progress made in the next few years is indicated by the size and capabilities of the four boats of the 'U19' class that were all delivered in 1913 from Danzig Dockyard as the Imperial German navy's first four diesel-engined submarines. These boats were each manned by 39 men, were 210.5ft (64.15m) long, possessed a surfaced and submerged displacement of 650 and 837 tons respectively, were capable of surfaced and submerged speeds of 15.5 and 9.5 knots respectively on their powerplant of 1,700hp (1,267.5kW) diesel engines or 1,200hp (895kW) electric motors, and carried an armament of one 86 or 105mm (3.4 or 4.1in) deck gun and four 17.7in (450mm) torpedo tubes.

The installation of the deck gun is signal evidence of a gradual shift in emphasis for the submarine's role. The torpedo was still seen as the primary weapon for the destruction of larger warships and merchant vessels at medium range, but was an expensive and bulky weapon of which only a relatively few could be carried. The deck gun, on the other hand, could be added without too much sacrifice of internal volume except for an ammunition magazine, and offered the possibility of comparatively cheap shell fire for the destruction of smaller naval vessels and larger merchant vessels. The rules of war dictated that the latter had to be stopped, searched and permitted to evacuate their crews and passengers before being sunk, and this was effectively impossible without the submarine surfacing, when the deck gun became a more cost-effective weapon than the torpedo.

Technical progress in the years before World War I (1914-18) was rapid, and by the beginning of the war there were about 400 submarines in service with 16 navies. The British and French mustered about half of this total, but whereas these vessels were generally of the small coastal type with

Below: The French *Gymnote* was the first successful modern submarine when it first appeared in 1888. In its original form the boat had virtually no superstructure and very poor depth-keeping capability, and was twice rebuilt to appear in 1898 to the form illustrated with a raised conning tower, an extended deck casing, and external drop collars for two torpedoes. In reality, however, the *Gymnote* was too small and rudimentary to be anything more than an experimental type.

Below left: These are the outline plans for the Holland-designed 'A' class submarine *Plunger*, later renamed as the A-1 and the lead boat of a seven-strong group that was the US Navy's first operational submarine class. The boats were completed between 1901 and 1903. All except the A-1 were transferred to the Philippines in 1909 and expended as targets in 1922, the year in which the A-1 was sold for scrap.

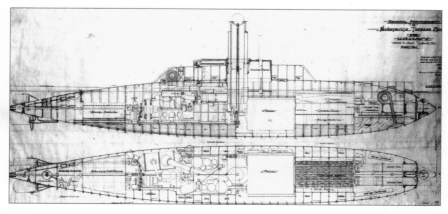

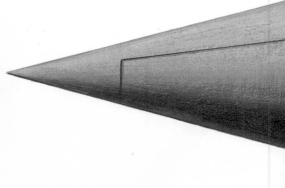

displacements of about 300 tons, the Germans used the larger type suitable for open-sea operations on a displacement between 550 and 850 tons. The Royal Navy had 71 operational submarines with another 31 being built, and the Germans had 33 with another 28 in production. The British and most other navies saw their submarines as companions to their large surface fleets used to scout and ambush the enemy's warships, but the Germans rapidly came to the conclusion that the submarine could and should be used as a deep-sea raider independent of the surface forces.

The first submarine operations of World War I were extremely limited, for none of the combatants had any experience in the use of such vessels under wartime conditions. The majority of navies and their senior officers viewed the submarine as an adjunct to their surface forces, which they deemed to be the real arbiters of any naval battle. Thus the submarine was seen primarily as a covert reconnaissance machine, and in the first days of the war the Germans sent some of their boats north through the North Sea to watch for the activities of the Grand Fleet, which was based on Rosyth and Scapa Flow in Scotland, while the British despatched some of their submarines into the south-east quadrant of the North Sea in the Heligoland Bight to watch for any sortie of the High Seas Fleet from its base at Wilhelmshaven. In the course of these initial operations the Germans lost two of the 10 boats they sent out: *U13* failed to return, probably as a result of hitting a mine, while *U15* was sighted, rammed and cut in two by a British cruiser.

Striking evidence of what might be achieved was soon provided by *U9*, which on one day sank the British armoured cruisers *Hogue*, *Aboukir* and *Cressy*, and then only three weeks later sank the cruiser *Hawke*: the British death toll was more than 1,600 men as well as four cruisers, albeit of types that were thoroughly obsolete and provided with indifferent protection against torpedo attack. Such was the fear of the submarine now instilled in the British that henceforward the major units of the Royal Navy ventured from port only when escorted by an outer screen of destroyers.

The British, and indeed all who sought to counter the threat of the submarine, were severely hampered by the lack of any means to detect a

Designed by the Reverend George Garrett and built in Liverpool during 1879, the *Resurgam* was an experimental submarine with steam power, but lacked weapons and was a bad depth keeper because of its lack of diving planes and the large size of its ballast tanks.

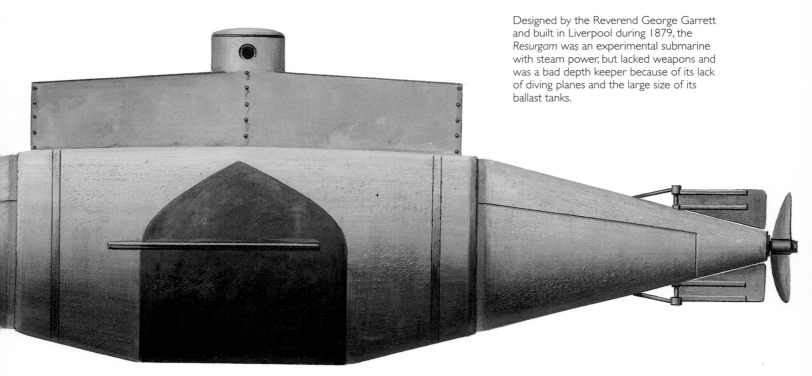

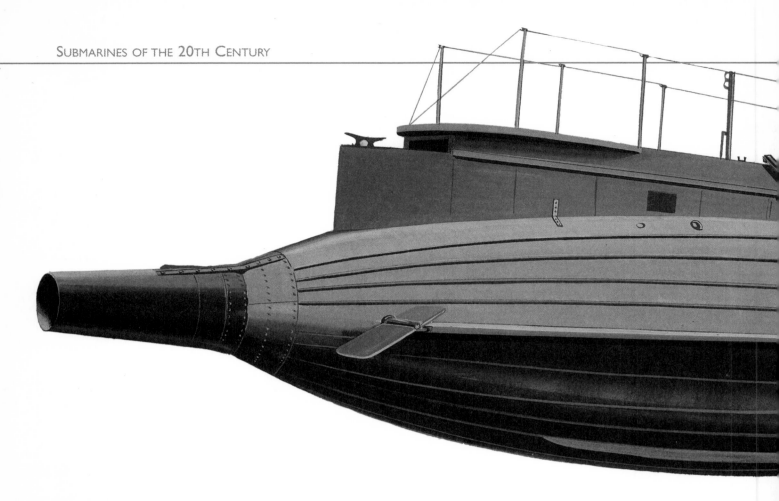

submerged submarine: only the sighting of a raised periscope, or the conning tower of a poorly trimmed boat breaking through the surface of the water, could provide advance warning of an event otherwise signalled by the thunderous explosion of a torpedo against the side of a hapless warship. Moreover, even when they sighted a submarine, the crew of a surface warship could achieve little in the way of securing the boat's destruction: new-construction destroyers and light cruisers were fitted with a reinforced foot on the stem for a ramming attack, and all vessels could respond with gunfire in the hope of holing the conning tower or carrying away a periscope.

The submarines of the period were just about fast enough on the surface to provide a scouting capability for forces of cruising warships but lacked the pace to keep up with them after these moved off at maximum speed, and they also lacked the underwater endurance and speed to serve as adjuncts to major surface forces except by lurking off the enemy's ports to report the sortie of such forces and perhaps torpedo one warship if the opportunity offered. Moreover, after a few brief flurries in 1914 and the first part of 1915, the British and German major fleets seemed content to remain in harbour and await the opportunity for a single climactic battle that would decide the outcome of World War I.

Thus there seemed little part for the submarine to play in the course of conventional naval warfare, so other methods were sought in which the new weapon could profitably be employed. Small numbers of submarines were detached to the confined waters such as the south-western corner of the North Sea, the Strait of Otranto and the Dardanelles,

Resulting from the development work carried out by the Norwegian armaments manufacturer Nordenfelt, this was one of two submarines built in Germany in 1890. The type was not successful, and little is known of its details, although it is thought that the bow-mounted 'snout' was probably a torpedo tube.

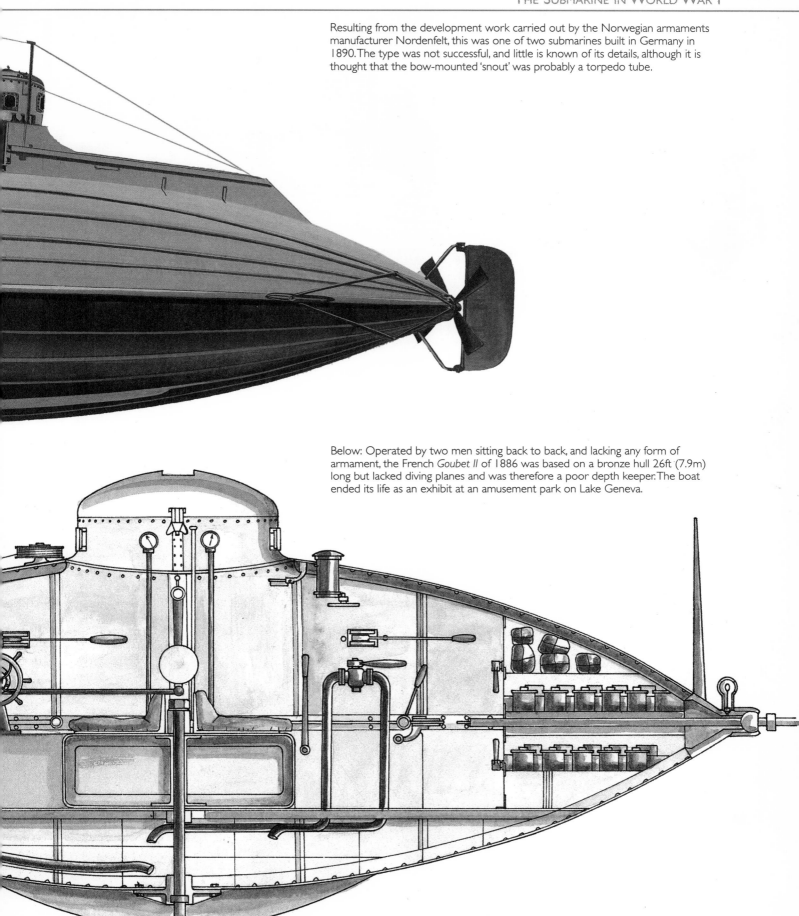

Below: Operated by two men sitting back to back, and lacking any form of armament, the French *Goubet II* of 1886 was based on a bronze hull 26ft (7.9m) long but lacked diving planes and was therefore a poor depth keeper. The boat ended its life as an exhibit at an amusement park on Lake Geneva.

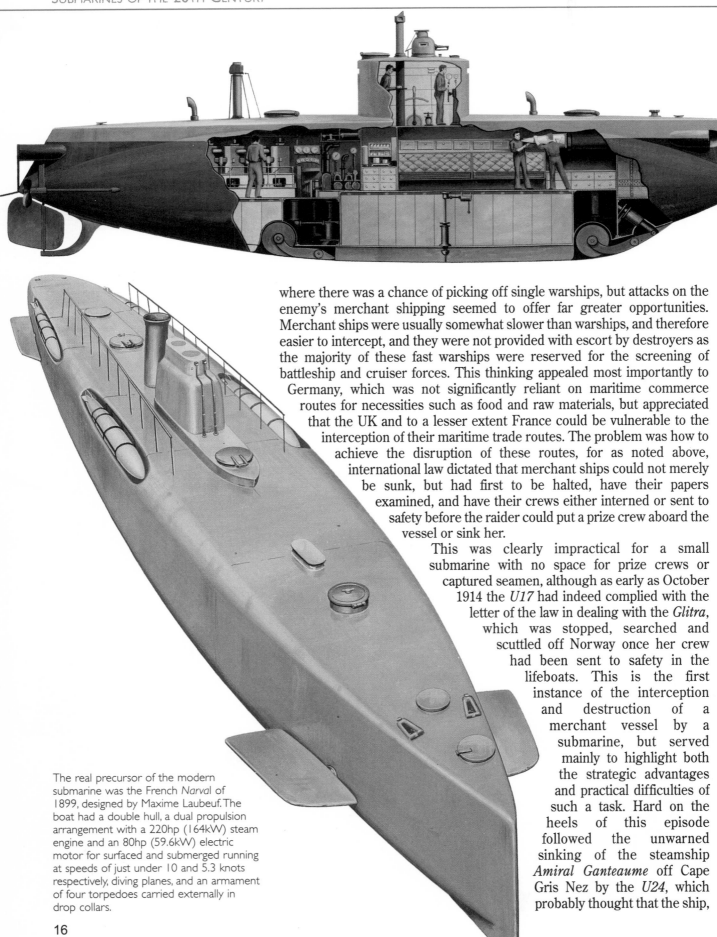

The real precursor of the modern submarine was the French *Narval* of 1899, designed by Maxime Laubeuf. The boat had a double hull, a dual propulsion arrangement with a 220hp (164kW) steam engine and an 80hp (59.6kW) electric motor for surfaced and submerged running at speeds of just under 10 and 5.3 knots respectively, diving planes, and an armament of four torpedoes carried externally in drop collars.

where there was a chance of picking off single warships, but attacks on the enemy's merchant shipping seemed to offer far greater opportunities. Merchant ships were usually somewhat slower than warships, and therefore easier to intercept, and they were not provided with escort by destroyers as the majority of these fast warships were reserved for the screening of battleship and cruiser forces. This thinking appealed most importantly to Germany, which was not significantly reliant on maritime commerce routes for necessities such as food and raw materials, but appreciated that the UK and to a lesser extent France could be vulnerable to the interception of their maritime trade routes. The problem was how to achieve the disruption of these routes, for as noted above, international law dictated that merchant ships could not merely be sunk, but had first to be halted, have their papers examined, and have their crews either interned or sent to safety before the raider could put a prize crew aboard the vessel or sink her.

This was clearly impractical for a small submarine with no space for prize crews or captured seamen, although as early as October 1914 the *U17* had indeed complied with the letter of the law in dealing with the *Glitra*, which was stopped, searched and scuttled off Norway once her crew had been sent to safety in the lifeboats. This is the first instance of the interception and destruction of a merchant vessel by a submarine, but served mainly to highlight both the strategic advantages and practical difficulties of such a task. Hard on the heels of this episode followed the unwarned sinking of the steamship *Amiral Ganteaume* off Cape Gris Nez by the *U24*, which probably thought that the ship,

Opposite: Rivalling John Holland as the father of the American submarine, Simon Lake produced the *Protector* in 1901 with extending wheels in the bottom of the hull so that the boat could travel along the sea bed. The boat was armed with three torpedo tubes (two in the bows and one in the stern), and was in most respects superior to the rival Holland No.8. It is possible that the US Navy ignored the *Protector*'s capabilities and greater 'developability' because of the oddity represented by the wheels, so Lake sold the boat to Russia, which then ordered another four. All five boats were shipped in sections to Vladivostok in eastern Siberia, and there assembled in time for service during the Russo-Japanese War (1904-05), in which they achieved nothing of note other than the deterrence of any Japanese naval attack on Vladivostok.

Right: The first submarine to be completed for the US Navy was the Holland-designed *Holland*, which was commissioned in 1900 with surfaced and submerged displacements of 64 and 74 tons respectively, a length of 53ft 9in (16.38m), a propulsion arrangement of one 45hp (33.5kW) petrol engine and one 50hp (37.3kW) electric motor for surfaced and submerged speeds of 8 and 5 knots respectively, a crew of 7, and an armament of one 18in (457mm) torpedo tube and one 8in (203mm) dynamite gun, although the original design had included two of each type. The boat was discarded in 1910.

Below: One of the Union's answers to the Confederacy's 'Davids' in the American Civil War (1861-65) was the Intelligent Whale, which was a carefully considered design that relied on manual propulsion, lacked a suitable weapon, was difficult to manoeuvre and, because of the war's end, was never used operationally.

in fact loaded with Belgian refugees, was a troopship and therefore a legitimate target.

The sinking of the *Amiral Ganteaume* was regarded by the Allies as a German atrocity, but was in fact a portent of the future for the submarine as World War I descended to the level of total war, in which the whole of the nation rather than just its armed strength was regarded as 'fair game'. In February 1915 Germany announced that the waters round the UK were now a war zone and that any British or French ship in it was liable to summary destruction without warning, and that as a result of the submarines' limitations (such as indifferent periscope quality) it was also impossible to guarantee the safety of neutral ships in the zone. The effect of this change soon made itself apparent: in January 1915 the British and French had lost 47,900 tons of merchant shipping, but after the declaration of the German war zone this total rose to 185,400 tons, 148,000 tons of it represented by British hulls.

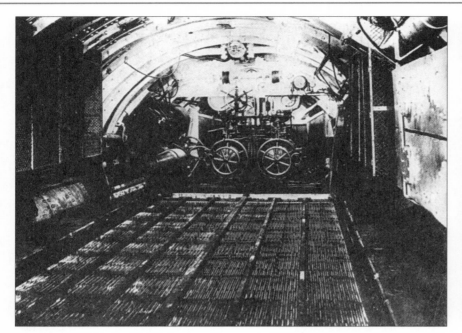

Above left: Seen in the early 1900s, this is the view looking forward in a Holland-designed 'B' class submarine, which was the second type of boat adopted by the US Navy as a development of the ideas embodied in the 'A' class. Visible are the side-by-side pair of 18in (457mm) torpedo tubes and, because the deck plates have been lifted, the batteries. The data for the three 'B' class submarines included surfaced and submerged displacements of 145 and 173 tons respectively, a length of 82ft 6in (25.15m), a propulsion arrangement of 250hp (186kW) petrol engines and a 150hp (112kW) electric motor for surfaced and submerged speeds of 9 and 8 knots respectively, and a crew of 10.

Left: The view aft from the control space in the 'B' class submarine is dominated by the engines for the single-propeller propulsion arrangement. The three boats were completed in 1906 and 1907, transported to the Philippines in 1912, and expended as targets in 1922.

Opposite: Completed in 1902, this is the Royal Navy's 'Holland' class submarine Holland No.4 photographed in 1904. Of the five boats, Holland No.1 and Holland No.2 were sold in 1913, Holland No.3 was sunk in experiments during 1911, Holland No.4 was dismantled in 1912, and Holland No.5 sank while on tow to the breaker's yard in 1912.

At this time the sole threat to Germany and its submarines was not British and French countermeasures, which were wholly ineffective, but the total opposition of world opinion, with that of America to the fore as its commercial interests were severely threatened. This hard-headed financial response to the threat of the German submarine offensive was strengthened by the weight of public opinion in May 1915, when the *U20* torpedoed the large liner *Lusitania*, which sank with the loss of many civilian lives including a number of Americans. This was not the first time in which civilians, particularly American civilians, had died as a result of submarine attack, but the scale of the losses combined with an astute British propaganda effort to swing American public opinion firmly behind the Allies paved the way for the USA's eventual entry into World War I in April 1917.

As the pace of the submarine war around the British and French coasts was increasing in the last months of 1914 and the first months of 1915, and as the Germans were preparing to shift toward a type of unrestricted submarine warfare not only in these areas but in the deeper waters of the North Atlantic Ocean, a relatively intense period of submarine warfare was becoming apparent in the Mediterranean. Most of France's submarines were located in this theatre, whose main base was Toulon in the south of France, but in the first months of the war there was little submarine activity as the British and French surface forces were sufficient to contain the considerably smaller and generally less effective navies of the Austro-Hungarian and Turkish empires. It was therefore left to the Austro-Hungarians, who initially possessed only seven submarines, to take the offensive in a bold attempt to redress the Mediterranean balance of naval power: in January 1915 the *XII* torpedoed and severely damaged the battleship Jean Bart, and four months later the *V* torpedoed and sank the armoured cruiser *Léon Gambetta*. By this time Turkey had entered the war, and after reinforcing her navally inept new partner with the *U21* sent into the Mediterranean via the Strait of Gibraltar, Germany decided that it would be more cost-effective to move six dismantled UB-type coastal submarines by rail to the Austro-Hungarian port of Cattaro (now Kotor), where they would be reassembled for operations under the German flag.

Three of the boats were then sent to Turkey, one disappearing *en route* and the other two reaching Constantinople (now Istanbul), where they joined forces with the *U21*, which in May 1915 torpedoed and sank the British battleships *Triumph* and *Majestic* off the Dardanelles. These elderly battleships had virtually no anti-submarine protection, but such was the fear

Above: Seen here as its crew wash it down while lying alongside *Holland No.4*, one of the four-strong second group of the 'Holland' class, the *Holland No.1* was the first submarine accepted by the Royal Navy after design by John Holland and construction by Vickers. The *Holland No.1* had surfaced and submerged displacements of 104 and 122 tons respectively, a length of 63ft 4in (19.3m), a propulsion arrangement of one 160hp (119kW) petrol engine and one 74hp (55.2kW) electric motor for surfaced and submerged speeds of 8 and 5 knots respectively, a crew of seven and an armament of one 14in (356mm) torpedo tube. The last four boats differed only in their submerged displacement of 150 tons and 250hp (186kW) petrol engine.

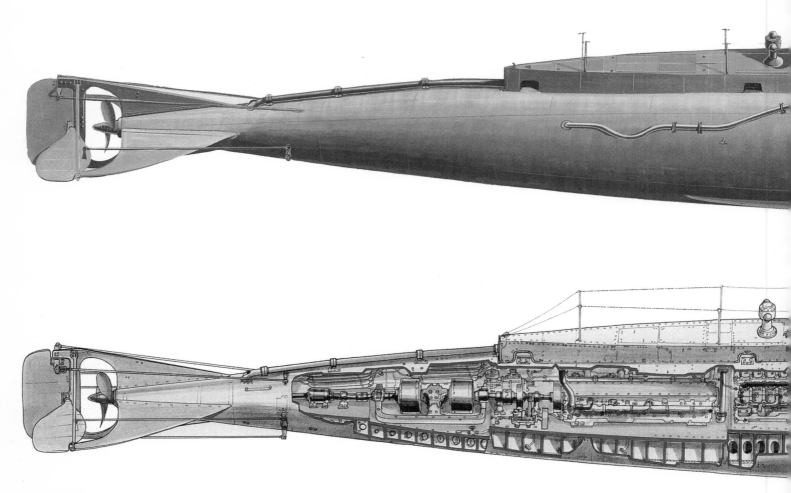

of submarine attack by the British naval forces off the Dardanelles that the local commander ordered all his larger warships back to anchor in the harbour of the Greek island of Mudros, thereby leaving the Allied infantry on Gallipoli with virtually no naval gunfire support.

By this time Italy had entered the war on the Allied side, and soon came to feel the effect of the new type of warfare as the submarines *Medusa* and *Nereide* and the cruisers *Amalfi* and *Giuseppe Garibaldi* were lost to submarine attack. Meanwhile, the squadron of six German boats in Turkey was continuing its run of success in the Black Sea and the Sea of Marmara. It was not all one-sided traffic, however, for the British and French respectively sent three and two obsolescent boats to blockade the mouth of the Dardanelles in case the Germans attempted to unleash their two most powerful ships in the area, the battle-cruiser Goeben and the light cruiser Breslau, which had reached Constantinople just before Turkey's entry into the war on the side of the Central Powers. The British then felt that it would be worth the effort to force their way past the Turkish anti-submarine defences in an effort to reach the Sea of Marmara, where they might find unwary Turkish targets.

This proved to be the case, and the *B11* there sank the old Turkish warship *Messudieh*. The Turkish ship was of no real operational value, but the fact that it had been reached and sunk encouraged the British to send no fewer than seven of the newer 'E' class boats to reinforce their submarine

Seen above in exterior and cutaway views, the Royal Navy's 'B' class of submarines totalled 11 boats all built by Vickers and completed in 1905 and 1906. The design represented what was basically the second stage of development from the original 'Holland' class of five boats via the 13 boats of the 'A' class also built by Vickers and completed between 1903 and 1905, but was limited by two factors. These were its small size, which made the boats capable of little more than harbour defence, and its use of petrol engines for surfaced running. The data for the class included surfaced and submerged displacements of 280 and 313 tons respectively, a length of 135ft 0in (41.15m), a propulsion arrangement of 600hp (447kW) petrol engines and a 190hp (142kW) electric motor for surfaced and submerged speeds of 12-13 and 7-9 knots respectively, a crew of 16, and an armament of two 18in (457mm) torpedo tubes in the bows. The B2 was lost during 1912 in a collision off Dover and the *B10* was bombed and sunk in 1916 in Venice harbour, but the other nine boats survived World War I (1914-18) to be sold and scrapped in the period after its conclusion.

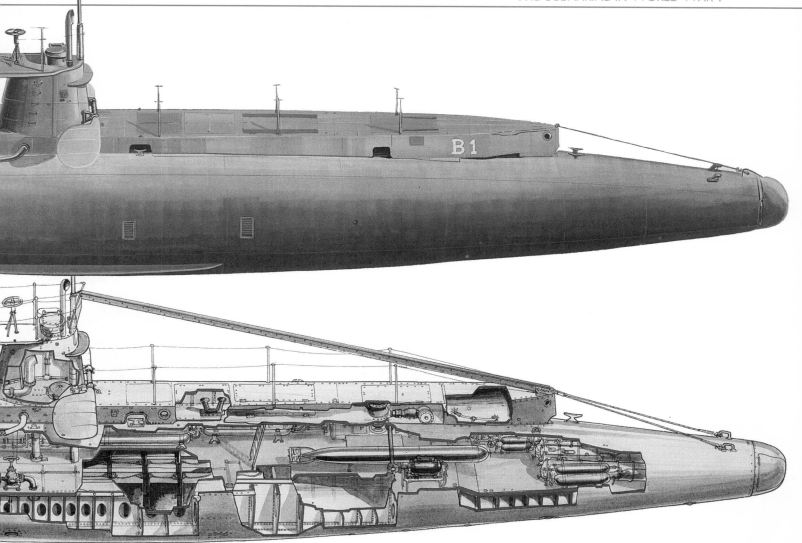

strength off Turkey. There followed a small but extremely brave and classic submarine campaign as these limited boats, complemented by a small number of French submarines, got through to the Sea of Marmara on several occasions and wrought considerable havoc in this Turkish 'pond'. Some of this havoc was wrought with torpedoes against larger ships, but much useful work was achieved with the submarines' newly provided deck guns against smaller ships and also upon Turkish trains plying the rail route along the coast. The Allied submarines continued to operate into the Sea of Marmara up to January 1916, when the Allies finally conceded the failure of their land campaign on each side of the Dardanelles and completed a superb amphibious evacuation.

The captains who had developed such skills were returned to the UK to continue their efforts in the North Sea, but the surviving submarines were used to strengthen the Allied force watching the mine barrage across the Strait of Otranto, which the Austro-Hungarian navy would have to penetrate in the course of any effort to break out into the Mediterranean.

The submarine campaign in the confined waters of the Strait of Otranto and around the Dardanelles was mirrored by a somewhat different campaign in the close, shallow and very heavily mined waters of the Baltic Sea, where the Germans faced the Russians, who were supported by a small number of British submarines. The first two out of three British boats despatched from a Scottish base arrived at the Russian base of Lapvik in the

Gulf of Finland during October 1914. Here the task of the British, and to a lesser extent the Russians (who were generally short of new submarines as the engines for their latest craft had been ordered from Germany), was not only to sink German ships but also to upset German fleet dispositions and training, of which the latter was habitually carried out in the 'safe' waters off the eastern end of the Kiel Canal and along the German Baltic coast. Even though the British boats at first enjoyed only limited success, this was sufficient to persuade the German naval commander-in-chief that the British had deployed at least a flotilla of submarines to the Baltic and that his two squadrons of large warships had to be retired to harbour until the flotilla's imagined depot ship had been located and destroyed.

Below: The US Navy's first submarine class, the seven boats of the 'A' class, slightly preceded the British 'Holland' class, which differed from the American original only in insignificant details. The 'A' class was notable for its fat cigar-shaped hull, very small deck casing, and vestigial conning tower.

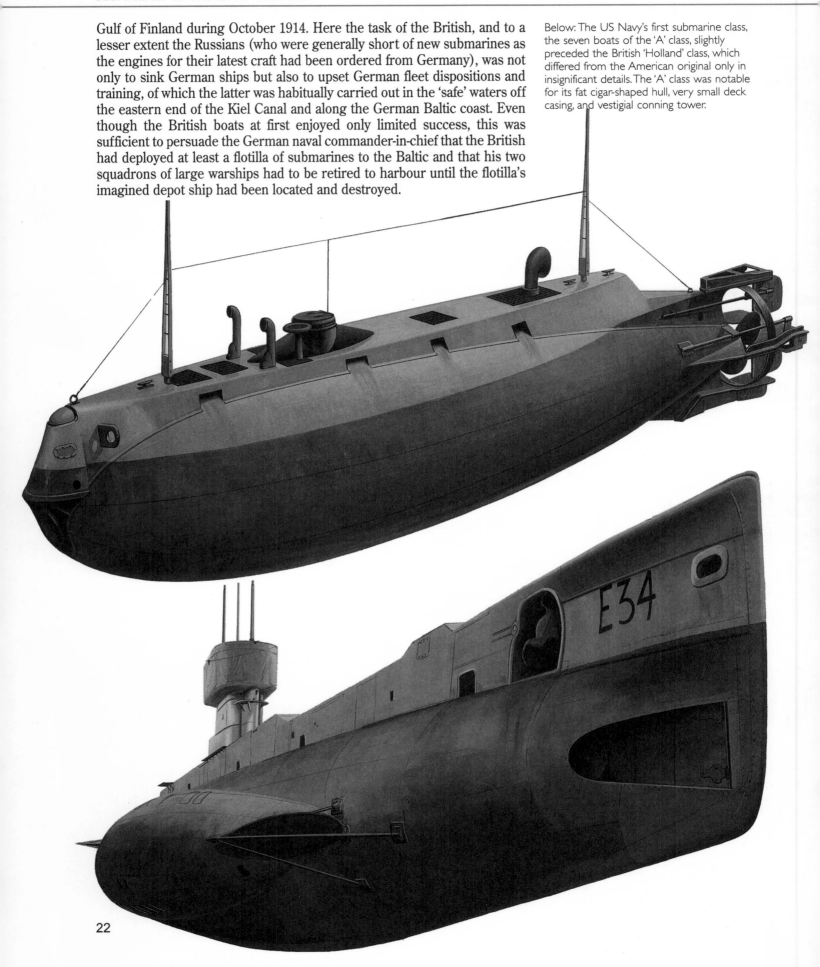

22

Opposite bottom: The 'E' class was the most successful British submarine type of World War I (1914-18), and was built to the extent of 55 boats including the *AE1* and *AE2* for the Royal Australian Navy. The class was built in three major subvariants (the 'E1', 'E7' and 'E21' types). Illustrated here is the *E34* completed in 1917 by Thornycroft as one of the six minelayers with the otherwise standard pair of 18in (457mm) beam torpedo tubes omitted to allow the incorporation of tubes for 20 mines. The submarine was lost in 1918 when it was itself mined in the Heligoland Bight.

This had an adverse effect on German naval planning, but more important was the success from the spring of 1915, when the Baltic unfroze, of the British boats on the merchant shipping used to transport high-grade iron ore from Sweden to Germany. A number of German warships were also attacked by Russian and British boats, and the success of the campaign in the Baltic soon persuaded the Admiralty to send additional boats to the Baltic. Four more 'E' class boats made the dangerous run through the Kattegat between Denmark and Norway/Sweden, one being lost in transit after running aground, while four older 'C' class boats sailed to the Arctic port of Arhangelsk, from which they were moved to Lapvik by rail and barge. By the late summer of 1915 the British and Russian submarine force

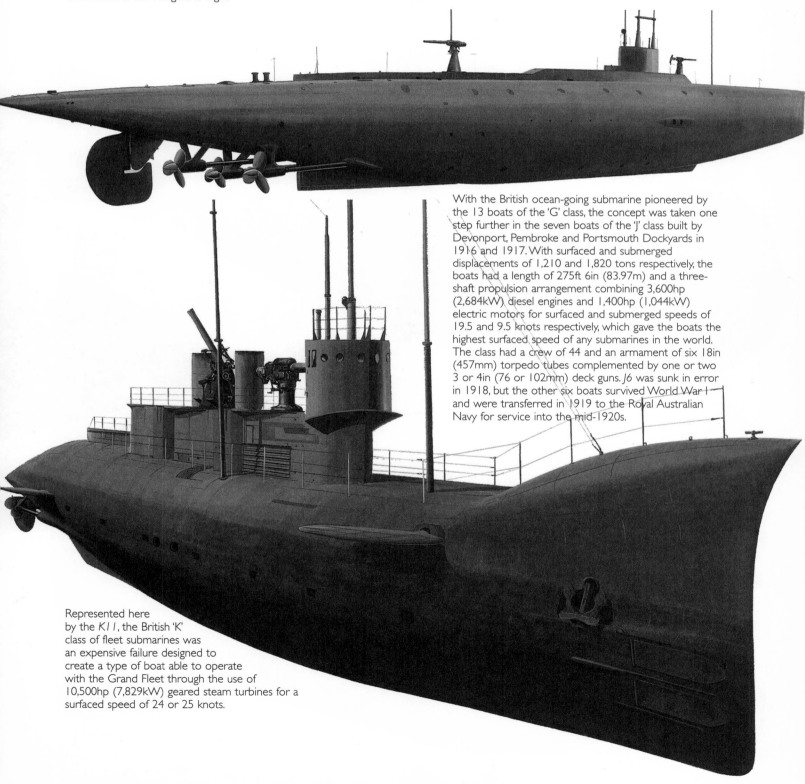

With the British ocean-going submarine pioneered by the 13 boats of the 'G' class, the concept was taken one step further in the seven boats of the 'J' class built by Devonport, Pembroke and Portsmouth Dockyards in 1916 and 1917. With surfaced and submerged displacements of 1,210 and 1,820 tons respectively, the boats had a length of 275ft 6in (83.97m) and a three-shaft propulsion arrangement combining 3,600hp (2,684kW) diesel engines and 1,400hp (1,044kW) electric motors for surfaced and submerged speeds of 19.5 and 9.5 knots respectively, which gave the boats the highest surfaced speed of any submarines in the world. The class had a crew of 44 and an armament of six 18in (457mm) torpedo tubes complemented by one or two 3 or 4in (76 or 102mm) deck guns. *J6* was sunk in error in 1918, but the other six boats survived World War I and were transferred in 1919 to the Royal Australian Navy for service into the mid-1920s.

Represented here by the *K11*, the British 'K' class of fleet submarines was an expensive failure designed to create a type of boat able to operate with the Grand Fleet through the use of 10,500hp (7,829kW) geared steam turbines for a surfaced speed of 24 or 25 knots.

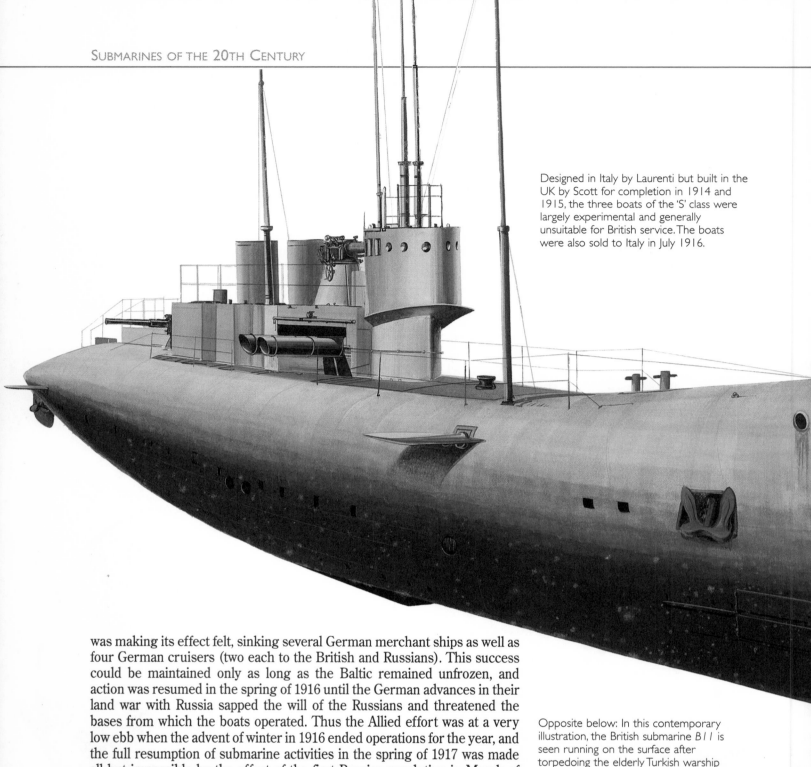

Designed in Italy by Laurenti but built in the UK by Scott for completion in 1914 and 1915, the three boats of the 'S' class were largely experimental and generally unsuitable for British service. The boats were also sold to Italy in July 1916.

was making its effect felt, sinking several German merchant ships as well as four German cruisers (two each to the British and Russians). This success could be maintained only as long as the Baltic remained unfrozen, and action was resumed in the spring of 1916 until the German advances in their land war with Russia sapped the will of the Russians and threatened the bases from which the boats operated. Thus the Allied effort was at a very low ebb when the advent of winter in 1916 ended operations for the year, and the full resumption of submarine activities in the spring of 1917 was made all but impossible by the effect of the first Russian revolution in March of that year. More concerned with internal matters and the continued land pressure exerted by the Germans, the Russians were unable to provide the technical support required by the British boats. There followed the second Russian revolution in November 1917 and the establishment of the communist regime, which reached a settlement with the Germans at Brest-Litovsk in the early part of the following year. As part of this settlement, the Soviets agreed to surrender the British submarines to the Germans, but before this condition could be exercised, an ice-breaker manned by anti-communist Russians opened a path into the Baltic from the base at Helsingfors (now Helsinki) so that the surviving submarines could be taken to deeper water and scuttled.

So far as the British and German naval commanders were concerned,

Opposite below: In this contemporary illustration, the British submarine *B11* is seen running on the surface after torpedoing the elderly Turkish warship *Messudieh* in December 1914. Despite the age and general inefficiency of the target, this was a remarkable feat for which the submarine had first to dive under five rows of mines and then escape in the face of gunfire and torpedo boat attack. The *B11*'s commander was awarded the Victoria Cross.

however, the Mediterranean and Baltic were side-show theatres compared with the North Sea, in which the two main protagonists, the British Grand Fleet and the German High Seas Fleet, confronted each other directly in a region that was generally accepted as being that in which the decisive naval engagement would be fought. In was for this theatre, therefore, that each side reserved its best boats and successively introduced its latest classes.

At the beginning of the war, the Germans had a modest number of boats in service in this theatre, and were building another 19 (*U31* to *U41* and *U43* to *U50*), with another six (*U51* to *U56*) soon ordered. All these boats were generally similar, with a displacement in the order of 720 tons, armament of four 19.7in (500mm) torpedo tubes located equally in the bow and stern, and a propulsion arrangement that combined two 1,100hp (820kW) diesel engines for surfaced running and two 550hp (410kW) electric motors for submerged running. It soon became clear that the torpedo was hardly a cost-effective weapon against the small coastal shipping that became the German submarines' main target, and the original 37mm gun, located on a retractable mounting, was rapidly replaced by a 3.465 or 4.13in (88 or 105mm) deck gun.

There followed the six, three and five boats of the '*U57*', '*U63*' and '*U66*' classes with a submerged displacement in the order of 830 tons, an armament of two or four bow and one or two stern tubes, all firing the 19.7in (500mm) torpedo, as well as a deck gun, and paired diesels and electric motors for surfaced and submerged speeds in the order of 15.5-17.5 knots and 8-9 knots respectively. These boats were known as the 'Mittel-U' types, and were the workhorses of the German submarine effort during 1915 and 1916.

This was not the limit of the German submarine-building effort, however, for in November 1914 it became clear that there would be no immediate victory on land and, faced with the prospect of a long war, the German naval high command decided to increase its submarine capabilities with two new types of boat, namely the 'UB' and 'UC' types optimised respectively for the coastal and minelaying roles. Both types were originally small, but they proved highly successful and were developed in later classes to considerably greater size and in these improved forms were generally superior in all operational respects to the 'Mittel-U' boats: the 'UB I' class, for example had a submerged displacement of only 142 tons and carried an armament of two 17.7in (450mm) torpedo tubes, while the final 'UB 133' class had a submerged displacement of 656 tons and carried an armament of five 19.7in (500mm) torpedo tubes and one 4.13in (105mm) gun; the 'UC I' class had a submerged displacement of only 183 tons and carried an armament of only 12 mines without any torpedo tubes, while the final 'UC III' class had a submerged displacement of 571 tons and carried an armament of three 19.7in (500mm) torpedo tubes, one 4.13in (105mm) gun and 14 mines.

The 'UB' boats proved very successful against coastal shipping and light warships in the waters around the coasts of the UK and northern France as well as in the central Mediterranean, while the 'UC' boats had an inauspicious start but then developed into highly successful types whose ability to lay new minefields quickly and accurately resulted in several spates of Allied losses.

The British followed a similar course to the Germans, but their construction programmes were generally a response to German leads

The *AE2* was one of two Royal Australian Navy 'E' class submarines built by Vickers and commissioned in 1914. The first boat was lost during 1914 in the Pacific, possibly after striking an uncharted reef, and this second boat was involved in the Dardanelles campaign, and was lost in 1915 after attacks by Turkish warships in the Sea of Marmara.

Opposite: *O-1*, seen here in a New York dry dock during 1918, was the lead boat of the 16-strong 'O' class of American coastal submarines completed in 1917 and 1918. The first two boats were built by Portsmouth and Puget Sound Navy Yards to provide the US Navy with experience in submarine construction, and the other 14 boats were built by commercial yards. The first 10 and last six boats formed two distinct subclasses, of which the lattes had a slightly longer but thinner hull, modestly reduced displacements, and an uprated propulsion arrangement. The basic data for the earlier subclass included surfaced and submerged displacements of 521 and 629 tons, a length of 172ft 3in (52.50m), a two-shaft propulsion arrangement combining 880hp (656kW) diesel engines and 740hp (552kW) electric motors for surfaced and submerged speeds of 14 and 10.5 knots, a crew of 29, and an armament of four 18in (457mm) torpedo tubes and one 3in (76mm) deck gun.

rather than the results of original thinking. Unlike the Germans, however, the British had started the war with a number of experimental types for the evaluation of new ideas: the three 'S' class boats were to an Italian design by Laurenti with diesel engines by Fiat, the four 'W' class boats were to a French design by Schneider-Lauboeuf, and the four 'V' class boats were to a Vickers design, while there were also the *Nautilus* and *Swordfish*, the former a large ocean-going boat and the latter a steam-powered boat designed to achieve greater surface speeds than was possible with current diesel-powered boats. After the outbreak of war, the Admiralty decided that the time for leisurely experimentation was past, and between October 1915 and August 1916 all seven units of the 'S' and 'W' classes were transferred to Italy.

The first response of the Admiralty to the outbreak of war and to the revelation that there would be no rapid outcome, was an order for an additional 38 boats of the successful 'E' class, supplemented by contracts to Canadian Vickers and the American yard at Fore River for a total of 20 'H' class boats using steel bought from the Bethlehem Steel Company. The boats were basically similar to the America's 'H' and Russian navy's 'AG' class boats, and a further eight boats were ordered from Canadian Vickers by Italy. The group of 10 American-built boats was finally released to the UK only after the USA's entry into the war in April 1917, and even then six of them were transferred to Chile in recompense for Chilean warships impressed by the British earlier in the war.

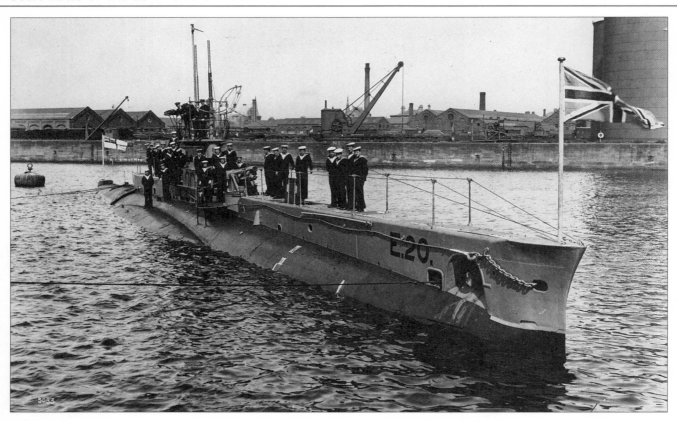

A member of the prolific 'E' class of British submarines, the E20 was the fourteenth and last of the 'E7' subclass, and was completed in 1915 after construction by Vickers. The boat was lost in the same year that it was commissioned, being torpedoed and sunk by the German coastal submarine *UB-14* in the Sea of Marmara.

As work on the 'H' class boats was starting, the Admiralty received reports (subsequently found to be erroneous) that the Germans were building a class of high-speed submarines, and decided to respond with its own class, which was to be capable of a surfaced speed of 20 knots and possess long-range radio, so that the boats could be used to create a reconnaissance line deep in the Heligoland Bight to watch for the emergence of the High Seas Fleet and instantly radio this information to the UK. The result was the seven-strong 'J' class, whose design included a length of more than 100ft (30.5m) – greater than that of the 'D' and 'E' classes – and a surfaced powerplant of three 1,200hp (895kW) Vickers diesel engines for a speed of 19.5 knots, which made them the fastest boats in the world.

The most unfortunate effect of the success of the 'J' class was the fact that it persuaded the Admiralty of the feasibility of using high-speed submarines as part of the main surface force. This led to the design and construction of the 17-strong 'K' class. This extraordinary type of 'fleet submarine', intended to scout for the Grand Fleet, was designed to exceed the maximum 21-knot speed of current battleships. Such a speed was clearly impossible with the current or even foreseeable generation of diesel engines, so Vickers designed the boat with a 10,000hp (7,456kW) geared turbine steam powerplant for surfaced propulsion at 24 knots. Moreover, the fleet task planned for these boats was further reflected in the armament, which included four fixed 18in (457mm) torpedo tubes in the bows, two trainable 18in (457mm) torpedo tubes on each beam to allow the engagement of targets off the submarine's high-speed surface course, and up to three guns including one anti-aircraft weapon.

The 'K' class boats were designed for entirely the wrong role, for the submarine had no place in close proximity to surface warships as it lacked the manoeuvrability and strength of its surface brethren, and naval personnel had so high a dread of submarine attack that they were likely to

Being small, technically complex and subjected to intense operational strains, submarines have always required considerable maintenance. There is little internal volume for the carriage of a large volume of spares, so the tendency has been for submarines to be supported by a depot ship providing specialist maintenance crews with well-equipped workshops and a large quantity of spares. The depot ships, such as that seen here with the British submarines *R2*, *R3* and *H3* alongside in World War I, also carried fuel and torpedoes to replenish her boats' bunkers and tubes, as well as comparatively spacious accommodation and recreation spaces for the crews of the boats alongside.

open fire as soon as they saw a submarine. This faulty tactical origin was matched by the complexity of the 'K' class design's propulsion arrangement, which was based on two steam boiler units each with its own funnel and air inlet. Before the boat could dive, therefore, the boiler had to be damped down, the funnels retracted, and all openings sealed against water ingress. It was, as one observer of the time said, a question of 'too many damned holes'. The 2,650-ton 'K' class boats were thus unsuccessful, as confirmed most unfortunately by the 'Battle of May Island' in January 1918 when *K22* (the renamed *K13* after the boat had foundered on its maiden voyage and had been raised) suffered a jammed helm while two flotillas of 'K' boats were exercising the battle-cruiser force: the *K4* rammed and sank the *K6*, and the *K17* was sunk by a cruiser.

After the completion of the *D1* as a semi-prototype with surfaced propulsion by diesel engines for the first time in a British submarine, the 'D' class was completed to a total of eight boats by another seven submarines to a slightly revised design with greater displacement, greater power for higher submerged speed, a larger conning tower, a revised deck profile and, for the first time in a British submarine class, a deck gun that was first installed on the *D4* (illustrated). The basic details for the 'D' class included surfaced and submerged displacements of 550 and 620 tons respectively, a length of 162ft 0in (49.38m), a two-shaft propulsion arrangement with 1,750hp (1,305kW) diesel engines and 550hp (410kW) electric motors for surfaced and submerged speeds of 16 and 10 knots respectively, a crew of 25, and an armament of three 18in (457mm) torpedo tubes and one (later two) 12pdr deck guns. The *D4* was notable for torpedoeing and sinking the German coastal submarine *UB-72* in the English Channel during May 1918.

German influence was also discernible in two other types of British submarine. After they had captured and examined a 'UC' type minelayer, the British modified six 'E' class boats to a similar capability with five mine chutes, each containing two mines, externally in each of the two ballast tanks rather than internally, the additional weight of the mining installation resulting in the omission of the two beam torpedo tubes that were otherwise standard in the 'E' class boats. Another British development was a response to the Germans' submarine cruisers, which were armed with 5.91in (150mm) guns for the destruction of small warships and merchant ships in the deep ocean areas. The Admiralty responded with an order for four 'M' class submarines each armed with a single turreted 12in (305mm) gun in addition to four 18in (457mm) torpedo tubes in the bows. In the event only three of these extraordinary boats were completed, only one of them in World War I, and two of these were lost in peacetime accidents.

During this period the large 'E' class (55 boats in three subvariants) had been proving its continued worth, and was followed by 36 units of the 'L' class, which was also produced in three subvariants as an enlargement of the 'E' class design and with a number of detail improvements.

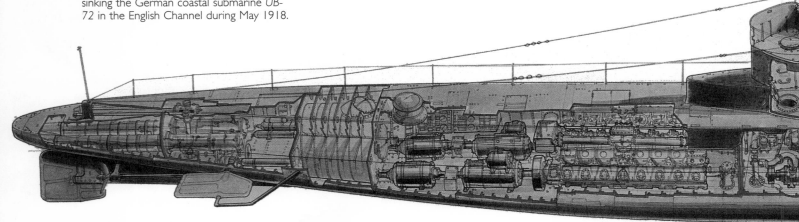

The British and, to a more limited extent, the Germans placed emphasis on the use of submarines with their surface fleets during World War I. Although it had not been established by May 1916, the month in which the climactic Battle of Jutland was fought, there should have been a flotilla of 12 submarines, based at Blyth in Northumberland and complemented by four destroyers for communications relay duties. This flotilla was to join the fleet 'in time to take part in a fleet action in the middle or southern part of the North Sea' and was to have two primary functions; firstly, operating 10 to 12 miles (16 to 19km) forward of the wing columns of the Grand Fleet, it was to attack the High Seas Fleet as it deployed and, secondly, any submarines that missed the German deployment were to press forward into the Heligoland Bight to make submarine interceptions of the Germans ships as they returned to harbour, or to undertake surface shadowings of German warships escaping laterally from the engagement. The German submarines had a similar function, and 18 boats were committed to the Jutland operation; three were submarine minelayers charged with laying fields off the Forth, the Moray Firth and to the west of the Orkney Islands, and the other 15 were tasked with the provision for reconnaissance and interception off the Grand Fleet's main harbours.

Below: The *U-31* was the lead boat of an 11-submarine class of sea-going submarines built by Germany and completed in 1914 and 1915. The *U-31* was itself lost in 1915, probably as a result of striking a mine in the North Sea. The basic details of the class included surfaced and submerged displacements of 685 and 878 tons respectively, a length of 212ft 4in (64.72m), a two-shaft propulsion arrangement with 1,850hp (1,380kW) diesel engines and 1,200hp (895kW) electric motors for surfaced and submerged speeds of 16.4 and 9.7 knots, a crew of 39, and an armament of four 19.7in (500mm) torpedo tubes and either one 4.1in (105mm) deck gun or two 3.4in (88mm) deck guns.

The last class of British submarines built in World War I was something of a departure from previous design concepts, for it was planned specifically for the hunter-killer role, seeking and destroying German submarines. Twelve of the class were ordered and 10 were completed to a very far-sighted design with a high length/beam ratio in a streamlined hull, single-shaft propulsion and enlarged battery capacity. This gave the boats the very high submerged speed of 14 knots, which was not exceeded by any submarine class until the closing stages of World War II, as well as longer submerged endurance at high speed: if a submarine detection system more effective than the hydrophone had been available, these 'R' class boats might very well have proved highly effective.

During this period German submarine construction had been proceeding apace. The well-established 'UB', 'UC' and 'Mittel-U' classes remained in production right to the end of the war, but further developments were increasing the capabilities of the German submarine arm. The first of these developments, ordered in January 1915, was the 'UE I' class of ocean minelayers, of which 10 were built with two longitudinal tubes (for 32 mines) rather than the vertically inclined tubes of the coastal minelayers. The class

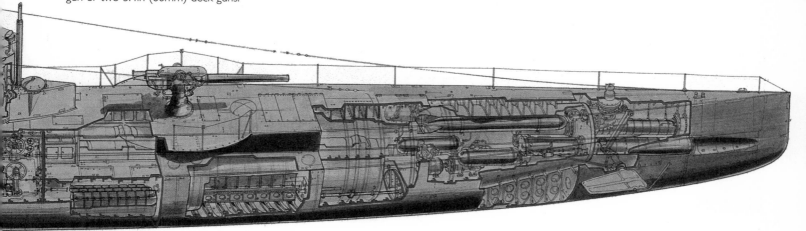

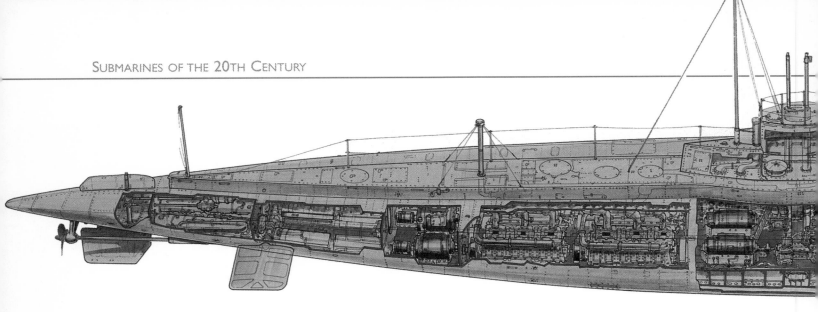

Above: Built in two four-boat subclasses constructed by the Germania and Danzig Dockyard during 1910 and 1911, the eight submarines of the 'U5' class were medium-size boats. All but one of the submarines were lost in World War I: the U5 was mined off Zeebrugge in 1914, the U6 was torpedoed off Stavanger in 1915 by the E16, the U7 was erroneously torpedoed in the North Sea during 1915 by the U22, the U8 was sunk in the Dover Strait during 1915 by British destroyers, the U9 (illustrated) became a surface minelayer in 1915 and a training boat in 1916 before being scrapped in 1919. The U10 was lost in the Baltic Sea during 1916 probably after hitting a mine, the U11 was mined in the Dover Strait during 1914, and the U12 was rammed and sunk off Fife Ness in 1915 by the British destroyer Ariel. The most successful of the boats was the U9, which sank the elderly British armoured cruisers Hogue, Aboukir and Cressy in a single engagement.

also possessed a lower length/beam ratio to allow a significant increase in bunkerage for considerably greater range. Although nicknamed the 'Children of Sorrow' and losing five of their number during the war, the boats of the 'UE I' class proved moderately effective and were followed by a further 10 boats of the improved 'UE II' class with the capability to operate off the eastern coast of the USA. These boats were considerably larger than their predecessors, and could carry 48 mines, no fewer than 24 torpedoes (12 internally and 12 externally) for the four 19.7in (500mm) tubes in the bows, and a gun armament of one 5.91in (150mm) or two 4.13in (105mm) weapons. Another eight of the class were scrapped late in the war before being completed, and it is possible to see in these boats the origins of the German submarines that proved so effective in World War II.

Although the success of the minelaying submarines was considerable, it was a success that did not directly seize the imagination of the naval authorities, and therefore greater attention was paid to the 'U-Kreuzer' types designed as submarine cruisers for long-range offensive operations against Allied shipping. This class resulted from the German realisation late in 1915 that it was often wasteful to use a torpedo against a target that could just as effectively be destroyed by surface gunfire, and the result was an initial order placed in May 1916 for the four boats of the 'U135' class; complemented in August of the same year by three boats of the generally similar but considerably larger 'U139' class. The 'U135' class had a submerged displacement of 1,535 tons and carried an armament of four

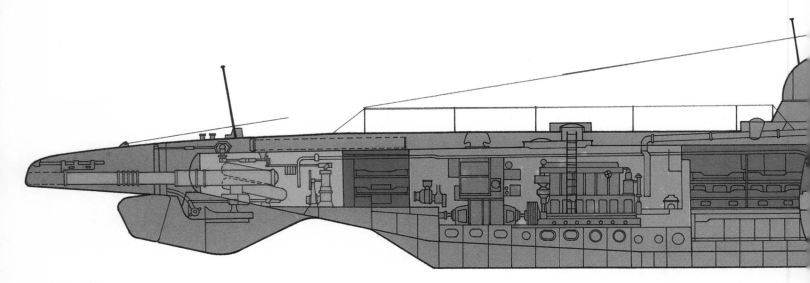

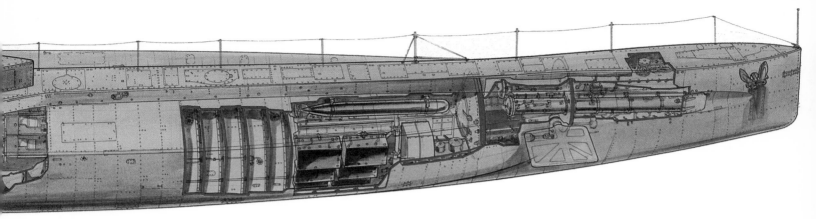

19.7in (500mm) bow torpedo tubes complemented, according to some sources, by two stern tubes of the same calibre, and also one 5.91in (150mm) deck gun, while the 'U139' class had a submerged displacement of 2,485 tons and an armament of six 19.7in (500mm) torpedo tubes (one bow and two stern) as well as two 5.91in (150mm) deck guns. An order was later placed for nine of the even larger 'U142' class with a submerged displacement of 2,785 tons and the same armament as the 'U139' class, but only one of these was completed, and it was scrapped in 1919.

The problem with these submarine cruisers was the fact that their greater size and armament were not really needed, for smaller submarines armed with a 3.465 or 4.13in (88 or 105mm) gun could achieve basically the same results on a hull that was cheaper and quicker to build, and which offered greater manoeuvrability. It might have been different if the additional size of the submarine cruisers had been used for significantly increased bunkerage for greater range, but as it was, the agility-sapping extra size was required mainly for the larger number of heavier guns and ammunition magazines.

It is worth noting that, as a result of the ever-tightening British naval blockade of her ports, which effectively halted all her maritime trade, Germany turned to the concept of the cargo-carrying submarine as a means of maintaining a trade in high-value freight. The first of these mercantile submarines was the *Deutschland*, which sailed from Kiel in June 1916 with a cargo of dyes, precious stones and mail. The submarine reached Baltimore

Below: The *U-26* was one of the 64-strong 'UC II' class of submarine minelayers completed in 1916 and 1917. The *U-26* was built by Vulkan in Hamburg, and was lost to British destroyer attack in the Thames estuary during 1917 while on a minelaying sortie. This inboard view reveals how much of the boat's forward section was occupied by the minelaying installation, which comprised six inclined tubes each carrying three mines. The rest of the armament comprised three 19.7in (500mm) torpedo tubes (one under the waterline at the stern and two above the waterline in the bow casing), and one 3.4in (88mm) deck gun. Other details of the class included surfaced and submerged displacements of 400-434 and 480-511 tons respectively depending on specific subvariant, a length of between 162ft (49.4m) and 173ft (52.7m) depending on specific subvariant, a two-shaft propulsion arrangement with 500-600hp (373-447kW) diesel engines and 460-620hp (343-462kW) electric motors for surfaced and submerged speeds of 11.5-12 and 6.6-7.4 knots respectively, and a crew of 26-28.

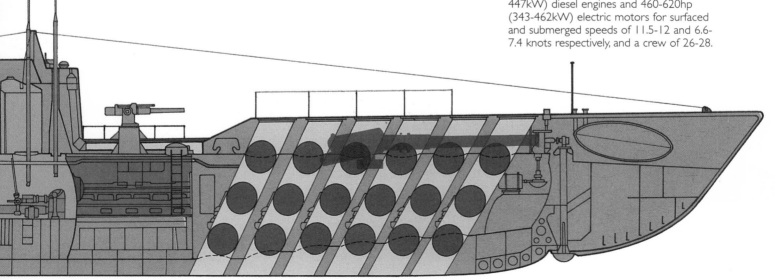

Completed in 1917 after being built by Weser at Bremen, the *UB-86* was one of the prolific 'UB III' class of coastal submarines of which 85 were completed up to the end of World War I. The *UB-86* survived the war and was surrendered to the British, who sold the boat for scrapping in 1921. Details of the 'UB III' class included surfaced and submerged displacements of 508-520 and 639-650 tons, a length of 182ft (55.5m), a two-shaft propulsion arrangement with 1,100hp (820kW) diesel engines and 788hp (588kW) electric motors for surfaced and submerged speeds of 13.5 and 7.5 knots respectively, a crew of 34, and an armament of five 19.7mm (500mm) torpedo tubes (four in the bows and one in the stern) together with one 4.1 or 3.4in (105 or 88mm) deck gun. The serrated structure over the bow was designed to facilitate the penetration of anti-submarine nets.

in the American state of Maryland just over two weeks later and, as it was entirely unarmed, it had to be treated as an otherwise conventional merchant vessel. After discharging the outward-bound load, the submarine took on a cargo of nickel, silver and zinc for the return voyage, which was achieved without incident. A second vessel of the second type, namely the *Bremen*, left on a similar voyage to Norfolk in the state of Virginia, but was lost without trace probably as the result of hitting a mine off the Orkney Islands.

The *Bremen*'s voyage had been planned in concert with a more offensive sortie towards the USA by the *U53*, which reached Newport, Rhode Island, in October 1916 to the great discomfiture of the Americans. The submarine later departed, and after leaving US territorial waters but within sight of an

American lightship began to attack Allied shipping. The Americans were furious, but were powerless to intervene before the submarine, after sinking five ships, finally headed for Germany. The whole escapade had been planned to frighten the USA into a retreat to strict neutrality, but signally failed to achieve this objective. The whole plan had been conceived within the concept of an all-out submarine offensive along the American east coast, but Kaiser Wilhelm II had refused to allow the implementation of the plan, and the whole concept of the mercantile submarine was therefore nullified. The Germany navy consequently ordered the conversion of the *Deutschland* into a submarine cruiser, and in February 1917 ordered another six boats with the standard armament two 19.7in (500mm) bow torpedo tubes, and two 5.91in (150mm) and two 3.465in (88mm) deck guns.

German submarine developments in World War I were completed by the small 'UF' and vast 'UD' class designs. The 'UF' class was designed for coastal operations in the Strait of Dover. With a submerged displacement of slightly under 300 tons and an armament of two 19.7in (500mm) bow torpedo tubes, the type was ordered to the extent of 92 units between December 1917 and July 1918, but none had been completed before Germany's defeat. The 'UD' class had a displacement of 4,000 tons and was intended for the submarine cruiser role with the same armament as the 'U151' class (converted mercantile submarines), but the type was cancelled as impractical. The only other type of submarine to enter service in World War I was the 'UA' class, which comprised a single small boat originally ordered by Norway.

Before the end of World War I in November 1918, Germany had ordered 811 submarines, 768 of this total resulting from orders placed during the war. More than 400 of this total were cancelled or scrapped while still uncompleted, and 178 other boats were lost. This represented some 47 per cent of the submarine arm's boats, and with the boats were killed 515

A member of the large 'UC II' class of German coastal minelayers, the *UC-71* was built by Blohm und Voss and completed in 1916. The boat saw considerable service in World War I, but sank in 1919 when on its way to surrender.

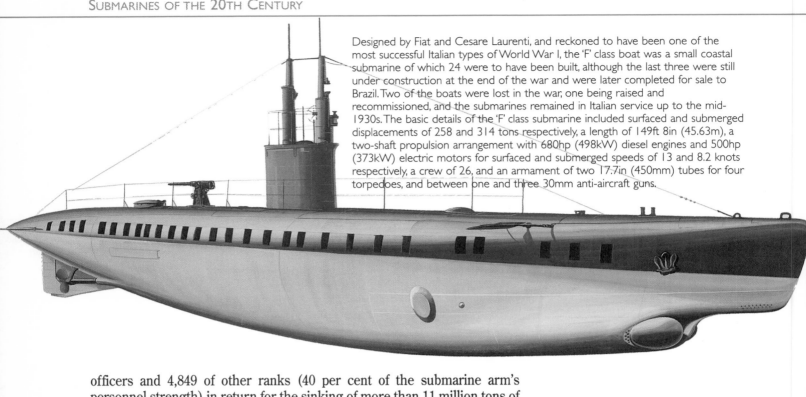

Designed by Fiat and Cesare Laurenti, and reckoned to have been one of the most successful Italian types of World War I, the 'F' class boat was a small coastal submarine of which 24 were to have been built, although the last three were still under construction at the end of the war and were later completed for sale to Brazil. Two of the boats were lost in the war, one being raised and recommissioned, and the submarines remained in Italian service up to the mid-1930s. The basic details of the 'F' class submarine included surfaced and submerged displacements of 258 and 314 tons respectively, a length of 149ft 8in (45.63m), a two-shaft propulsion arrangement with 680hp (498kW) diesel engines and 500hp (373kW) electric motors for surfaced and submerged speeds of 13 and 8.2 knots respectively, a crew of 26, and an armament of two 17.7in (450mm) tubes for four torpedoes, and between one and three 30mm anti-aircraft guns.

officers and 4,849 of other ranks (40 per cent of the submarine arm's personnel strength) in return for the sinking of more than 11 million tons of Allied shipping, including British losses of more than 2,000 ships with more than 14,000 merchant mariners.

The critical point in the submarine campaign came in February 1917, when the Kaiser reluctantly agreed to the launch of a campaign of unrestricted submarine warfare against the shipping which plied between the Allied nations. This campaign came as an enormous blow to the Allies in Germany and the UK in particular, and during April 1917 the merchant shipping tonnage lost to submarine attack increased to 881,000 tons, representing one ship in every four bound for a British port. The effect of the campaign was so profound that it was calculated at this time that the UK had food reserves for only six weeks, and the country therefore faced the prospect of starvation or an accommodation with the Germans.

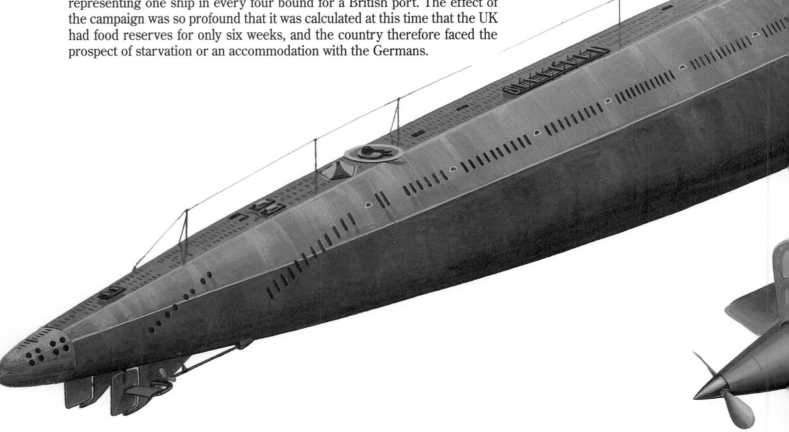

In the event, the launch of the unrestricted submarine warfare campaign was the fact that finally sealed Germany's defeat. Long exasperated by Germany's attitude, which included an apparent attempt to foment an anti-American revolution in Mexico, the start of the new campaign was the final straw for the USA, which declared war on Germany in April 1917. There was little that the USA could achieve in the short term to aid the European Allies except to increase the flow of food and other supplies, and to undertake limited anti-submarine measures in the western half of the Atlantic, but this coincided with the belated British introduction of the convoy system, which rapidly proved itself the best method of defence against submarine attack. Although the Admiralty had long argued against the system, on the grounds

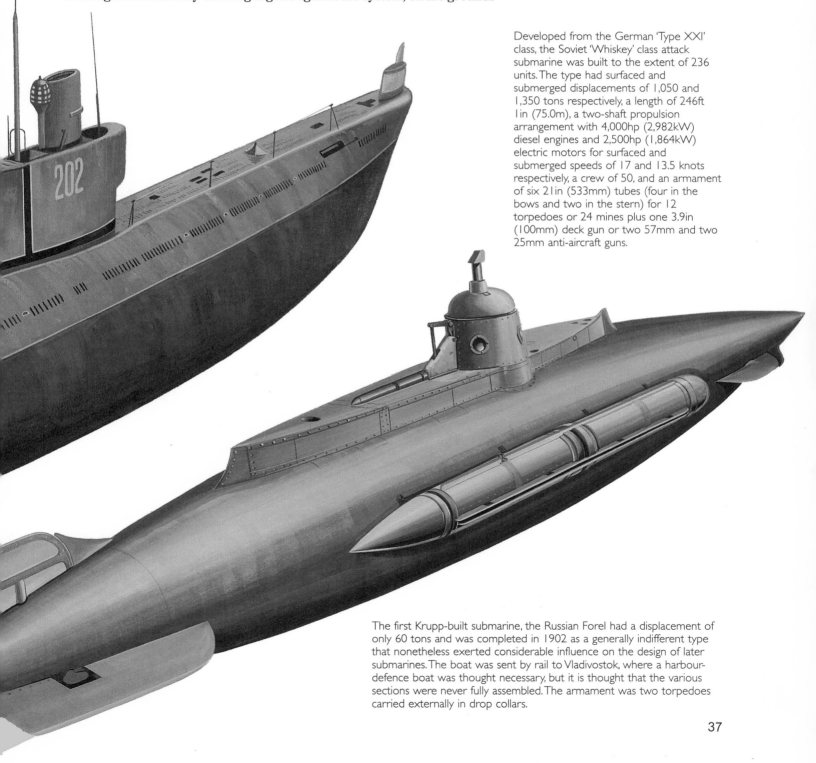

Developed from the German 'Type XXI' class, the Soviet 'Whiskey' class attack submarine was built to the extent of 236 units. The type had surfaced and submerged displacements of 1,050 and 1,350 tons respectively, a length of 246ft 1in (75.0m), a two-shaft propulsion arrangement with 4,000hp (2,982kW) diesel engines and 2,500hp (1,864kW) electric motors for surfaced and submerged speeds of 17 and 13.5 knots respectively, a crew of 50, and an armament of six 21in (533mm) tubes (four in the bows and two in the stern) for 12 torpedoes or 24 mines plus one 3.9in (100mm) deck gun or two 57mm and two 25mm anti-aircraft guns.

The first Krupp-built submarine, the Russian Forel had a displacement of only 60 tons and was completed in 1902 as a generally indifferent type that nonetheless exerted considerable influence on the design of later submarines. The boat was sent by rail to Vladivostok, where a harbour-defence boat was thought necessary, but it is thought that the various sections were never fully assembled. The armament was two torpedoes carried externally in drop collars.

that it concentrated targets for submarine attack, it was soon proved that the concentration of defence provided by the escort warships was greater than the concentration of opportunity offered to the German submarines, and sinkings soon declined to a significant degree (257 out of 84,000 convoyed ships, or 0.4 per cent, compared with 2,616 independently sailed ships), especially after the Americans were able to provide a measure of protection on their side of the Atlantic ocean.

The failure of the unrestricted submarine warfare campaign coincided with the threatened arrival of vast American armies, in France to bolster the steadily growing Allied offensive capability. This persuaded the German armies to launch their final desperate offensives during the spring of 1918, just before the main weight of the American forces began to make its presence felt, and the failure of these offensives sealed Germany's ultimate defeat.

The world's first submarine minelayer, the Russian *Krab* was built at Nikolayev on the Black Sea. Although laid down in 1908, the boat was not completed until 1915, when it had been rendered obsolete by more recent German submarine minelayer developments. The boat had two long ducts along the length of the upper casing, and the mines were moved to the rear along these ducts by a conveyor belt system that dropped the mines over the stern through a pair of hatches. The boat encountered many teething problems but nonetheless managed to lay some successful fields in the Black Sea before being scuttled by the British in 1919. The wreck was raised by the Soviets in 1935 and then scrapped.

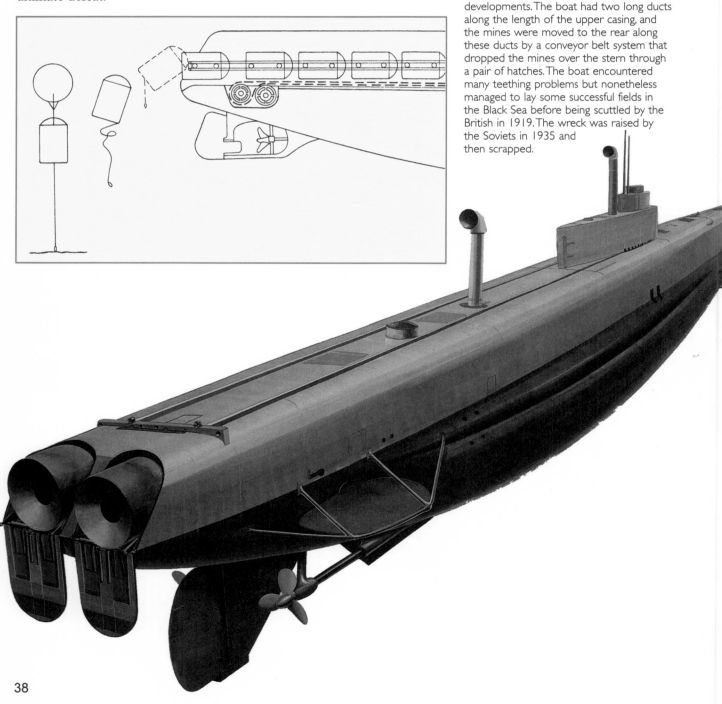

Lessons Forgotten – The Submarine Between the World Wars

Designed as a portly ocean-going replenishment type to supply operational boats with oil fuel and torpedoes in mid-Atlantic, the 'Type XIV' was built to the extent of six boats by Deutsche Werke at Kiel. All six boats were lost to Allied attack in 1942 (one boat) and 1943 (five boats). The basic specification included surfaced and submerged displacements of 1,688 and 1,932 tons respectively, a length of 220ft 3in (67.1m), a two-shaft propulsion arrangement with 2,800hp (2,088kW) diesel engines and 750hp (559kW) electric motors for surfaced and submerged speeds of 14.5 and 6.25 knots respectively, a crew of 53, an armament of two 37mm and one 20mm anti-aircraft gun, and provision for a cargo that included 432 tons of oil fuel and four torpedoes, the latter carried as deck cargo.

A s the major powers emerged from World War I in the last months of 1918, most of them were exhausted both financially and spiritually, and were determined to ensure that nothing of a similar magnitude could occur again. One of the major factors they had to take into consideration was the submarine, and evidence of its importance in World War I was provided by the revelation that the UK, the world's major maritime power, had lost more than 9 million tons of mercantile shipping, representing some 90 per cent of its pre-war tonnage, within the context of total Allied losses of more than 13 million tons.

The effect of these losses on Allied thinking were enormous, and a clause of the Armistice agreement with Germany stipulated that all seaworthy German submarines were to be surrendered at designated Allied ports, while unseaworthy boats were to be immobilised and disarmed in German ports pending the arrival of Allied inspection teams. Germany thus surrendered 176 boats, with others preferring internment in neutral ports, and the Allies quickly set about an evaluation of the weapon that had nearly defeated them. Germany surrendered 105 boats to the British, who operated at least three of them for evaluation purposes, 46 to the French who took 10 of them into their own service, seven to the Japanese who took them all into service, 10 to the Italians, and six to the Americans. The Belgians received two boats originally surrendered to the British. With the

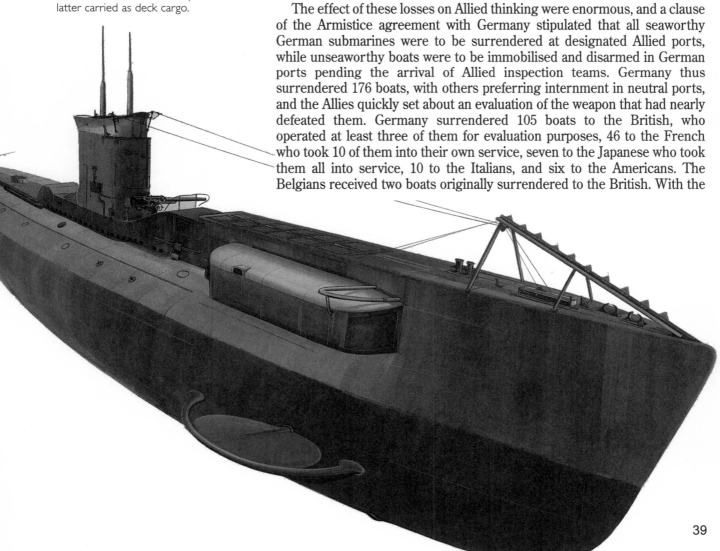

exception of the French boats, all of these surrendered craft were destroyed by inter-Allied agreement in 1922 and 1923, but by this time all possible implications of German design practices had been gleaned.

Oddly enough, given the fact that its general clumsiness and overgunning were readily apparent, the major Allied powers decided that the German submarine cruiser concept had considerable merit and therefore started on the development of such boats for their own submarine arms. This tendency was exacerbated by the fact that the two navies that received more than their 'share' of the German spoils, namely those of the USA and Japan, were expanding rapidly and considered the submarine cruiser ideal for operations in the vast oceans that were their primary theatres of operation. The Americans incorporated many features of the U140 in their 'V' class boats, which comprised the three boats of the 'Barracuda' subclass and the six other boats that constituted four subclasses. All these boats were notable for their very long range, considerable complements of 21in (533mm) torpedoes, and large-calibre deck gun comprising one 5in (127mm) weapon in all but the *Narwhal* and *Nautilus*, which each carried two 6in (152mm) weapons. Among the last six boats was the *Argonaut*, which was a further development incorporating the type of minelaying capability (60 mines) of which the Americans learned from another German submarine, the 'UE II' class *U117*.

The Japanese moved into the submarine cruiser field with the *I-52*, derived from the 'UE II' class boat *U125* which the Japanese had placed in service as the *O-1*. The Japanese followed the *I-52* with the four submarines of the 'Type J1' class, each of which had a submerged displacement of 2,790 tons, a range of 24,400 miles (39,265km), and an armament of six 21in (533mm) tubes with 20 torpedoes, and two 5.5in (140mm) deck guns. Although derived from the 'UE II' class, these boats had no minelaying capability, which was then incorporated in the succeeding but

somewhat smaller 'Type KRS' class, of which four were built with provision for 42 mines as well as a standard armament of four 21in (533mm) tubes with 12 torpedoes, and one 5.5in (140mm) deck gun.

The British also acquired an interest in the submarine cruiser, and moved into this area of operation with the *X1*, a further development of the Germans' uncompleted 'U173' class of very large submarine cruisers, which was armed with four 5.2in (132mm) guns in two paired mountings as well as six 21in (533mm) tubes for 12 torpedoes. The British even went so far as to adopt a pair of German diesel engines for surface running, but these proved to be plagued by unreliability and other problems, and the *X1* was scrapped after only five years, taking with it British interest in the submarine cruiser concept.

Of the European nations, this left only France as an adherent of the submarine cruiser concept. The French opted for a boat built with the largest-calibre gun permitted by the Washington Naval Treaty of 1922, namely 8in (203mm). The result was the large *Surcouf*, which carried two 8in guns in a trainable turret, eight 21.7in (550 mm) tubes for 18 torpedoes, and a mounting for four 15.7in (400mm) tubes for eight specialised anti-ship torpedoes. The boat also had provision for a small scouting floatplane, which could be dismantled for carriage in a small watertight hangar, and provision for the incarceration of 40 prisoners.

The French *Surcouf* was the greatest of all the submarine cruisers, and was notable for its great endurance, turreted pair of 8in (203mm) guns, and accommodation for the crews of captured ships.

In the early 1920s serious consideration was given in the Washington Naval Treaty to the banning of the submarine, and this was a notion that the British, with their losses to submarine attack in World War I still fresh in their minds, fully approved. The French and Italians, on the other hand, saw the submarine as a comparatively cheap yet effective weapon with which they could come to rival the larger powers, and therefore pressed for the type's retention. So too did the Japanese, who saw in the type a means of offsetting the Americans' superiority in large surface warships. The result of these machinations was that the submarine was not banned, but merely limited to the same 8in (203mm) main gun calibre as the heavy cruiser. And as a result of French pressure, no limit was fixed on the numbers of submarines that each of the powers was allowed to build, and unrestricted submarine warfare was not outlawed. An immediate result was that the world's major navies, restricted by treaty in the numbers and sizes of the major warships they might build, turned their attentions to the large-scale manufacture of submarines, and the world's smaller navies also

stepped up the pace of their submarine programmes. Of these smaller navies, the most adventurous were the Danish, Dutch, Norwegian, Polish and Swedish, of which all but the Norwegians opted for indigenous as well as imported designs.

The most far-sighted of these nations, so far as technical innovation was concerned, were the Dutch. In 1937 their 'O21' class introduced a breathing mast so that the diesel engines could be run when the submarine was just below the surface of the water, thereby allowing the batteries to be charged. This important development received little acclaim, and indeed the masts were removed by the British when some of the boats escaped the defeat of the Netherlands in May 1940 and reached the UK. It was only later in the war, when the Germans discovered parts of such a mast in a Dutch shipyard, that its full value was appreciated: the Germans developed the concept into the *Schnorchel* that allowed their boats to travel just under the surface for protracted periods, therefore receiving less attention from the rampant Allied anti-submarine aircraft.

The exaggerated importance attached to the submarine as a major force in modern war is nowhere better attested than in the suggestion put before the French parliament in 1920; that the French navy procure a fleet of between 250 and 300 submarines not only to replace the navy's current force of battleships and cruisers, but also to expand France's overall naval capabilities. The submarine's popularity had suffered a severe reverse in the later stages of World War I, the French navy argued, and a balanced force of surface vessels and submarines was needed, and it was this reasoned view that prevailed. The French navy therefore started a major programme of submarine construction based on two core types, namely the first-class submarine with a displacement of about 1,000 tons for ocean and overseas offensive/defensive use, and the second-class submarine with a displacement of some 600 tons for home-based defensive use. The first-class submarines comprised the nine units of the 'Requin' class, and the 29 units of the '1,500-tonne' class in several subvariants that were to have been replaced in the early 1940s by the 14 units of the 'Roland Morillot' class. The second-class submarines comprised the 10 units of the 'Ariane' class in three subvariants, and the 22 units of the 'Amazone' class in five subvariants. Finally ,there were the six submarine minelayers of the 'Saphir' class.

A country that was left out of the international naval planning of the 1920s was the USSR, which emerged from the collapse of Russia with a considerable fleet of World War I submarines of which only a few were serviceable in the early 1920s (10 in the Baltic, one in the Arctic and five in

Built by Blohm und Voss in Hamburg, the *U-1407* was a 'Type XVIIB' class coastal submarine with Walther propulsion. The boat was scuttled in May 1945 but later raised for trials in Royal Navy hands as the N25 that later received the name *Meteorite*. The 'Type XVIIB' class had surfaced and submerged displacements of 312 and 357 tons respectively, a length of 136ft 3in (41.5m), a single-shaft propulsion arrangement with 2,500hp (1,864kW) Walther geared turbines for a speed of 21.5 knots together with a subsidiary plant of 210hp (156.5kW) diesel motor and 77hp (57.4kW) electric motor for surfaced and submerged speeds of 8.5 and 5 knots respectively, a crew of 19, and an armament of two 21in (533mm) tubes for four torpedoes.

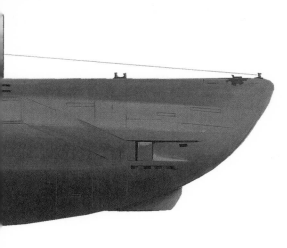

the Black Sea). Soviet military developments during the remainder of the 1920s were confined mainly to the army and air force, together with a limited refurbishment of existing naval units, and it was 1931 before the navy received any new submarines, in the form of the six units of the 'D' class based on an Italian design and then 24 units of the 'L' class based ultimately on the British 'L' class of World War I; one of these boats had been sunk during the Allied intervention in the USSR in 1919, was raised in 1928 and recommissioned into the Soviet navy in 1931. The last of the resulting 'L' class boats was not commissioned until 1942.

These two types were of moderately large size, and further capability was provided by smaller boats optimised for the coastal defence role. These boats included 90 units of the 'Shch' class commissioned between 1933 and 1942, 33 units of the 'Stalinets' class commissioned from 1936, and three units of the 'Pravda' class also commissioned from 1936. The 'Pravda' class boats were very good, possibly because the design was based on the German 'Type IA' class created by one of the clandestine teams that Germany established in the Netherlands, Spain and the USSR to maintain an uninterrupted submarine-designing capability despite the ban on such activities imposed by the Treaty of Versailles in 1919.

These boats represented the most important elements of the Soviet submarine fleet and occupied the intermediate-displacement sector of the size spectrum. The USSR also favoured smaller and larger submarines, however, the former represented by the 'Malyutka' class with a displacement of only 160 tons and an armament of two 21in (533 mm) torpedo tubes, and the latter by the 'Katyusha' class optimised for the submarine cruiser role with a displacement of 1,390 tons and an armament of ten 21in torpedo tubes plus two 3.93in (100mm) and two 45mm deck guns. Production of the 'Malyutka' class deck amounted to more than 50 boats in the period between 1933 and 1937, with more units of two later subvariants added between 1938 and 1944, and deliveries of the 'Katyusha' class amounted to at least 13 boats between 1940 and 1942.

Completed in September 1915 after being built by Electric Boat at Fore River, the *M-1* was the first double-hull submarine, and survived to 1922 before being sold out of the service. The boat had surfaced and submerged displacements of 488 and 676 tons respectively, a length of 196ft 3in (59.82m), a two-shaft propulsion arrangement with 840hp (626kW) diesel engines and 680hp (507kW) electric motors for surfaced and submerged speeds of 14 and 10.5 knots respectively, a crew of 28, and an armament of four 18in (457mm) torpedo tubes and one 3in (76mm) deck gun.

Having failed in their attempt to have submarines banned by the Washington Naval Treaty in 1922, the British decided that they had to compete in this important field and in 1923 launched a major programme of design and construction based on the 'L' class of 1917. This resulted in the 'O' class that had greater length and beam than the 'L' class but the same primary armament of eight 21in (533mm) tubes located as six in the bows and two in the stern with a total of 16 torpedoes. Power remained essentially unaltered even though the size and displacement had increased, so the maximum attainable surfaced and submerged speeds were reduced, although this was offset by the greater range provided by enlarged bunkerage. Further development of the same basic design resulted in the slightly larger 'P' and 'R' classes.

The next British development was the 'River' class, of which six were built from 1929 and with a surfaced speed of 22 knots. This was made possible only by the introduction of larger diesel engines, which required the omission of the stern torpedo tubes, but it soon became clear that the boats, although successful in the technical sense, had been created to a flawed operational concept as there was really little need for a submarine with a high surfaced speed except for commerce-raiding sorties in the Pacific Ocean, in which the Royal Navy had little interest at the time.

Over much the same period, the British commissioned six 'Porpoise' class submarine minelayers each with a complement of 50 mines in an external casing. Again, these boats proved successful at the technical level but were in this instance rendered superfluous by the British development of a mine type that could be laid through the tubes of standard submarines. Even so, the 'Porpoise' class boats proved their worth in 1941 and 1942, when they were operated as supply submarines running essential equipment and food into the beleaguered island fortress of Malta.

By the late 1920s, the Royal Navy had decided that its current types of patrol submarines were basically too large for successful employment in European and Mediterranean waters, and therefore undertook the development of a new and smaller type as the 'S' class, of which some 60 units were subsequently completed with a standard armament of six 21in (533mm) torpedo tubes in the bows. Other than its reduction in size, the most important improvement in the 'S' class over the preceding classes was the incorporation of all bunkerage inside the pressure hull, thereby removing the type of 'telltale' oil leaks that had bedevilled the earlier classes with their external bunkerage.

A truly remarkable but generally unsuccessful type, the British 'M' class comprised two boats completed in 1918 by Vickers and a third unit completed in 1920 by Armstrong Whitworth. The M1 sank in 1925 after a collision at sea, the M2 was altered to carry a seaplane and foundered in 1932, and the M3 was altered to a minelayer and was sold in 1932.

The 'S' class, of which 62 were completed between 1932 and 1945, was one of the most successful British submarine types of World War II and was used for offensive operations in home waters, the Mediterranean and the Far East. The second group, to which all but the first 12 boats belonged, was characterised by surfaced and submerged displacements of 715 and 990 tons respectively, a length of 217ft 0in (66.14m), a two-shaft propulsion arrangement with 1,900hp (1,417kW) diesel engines and 1,300hp (969kW) electric motors for surfaced and submerged speeds of 14.75 and 9 knots respectively, a crew of 44, and an armament of seven 21in (533mm) torpedo tubes and one 3in (76mm) deck gun.

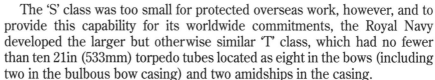

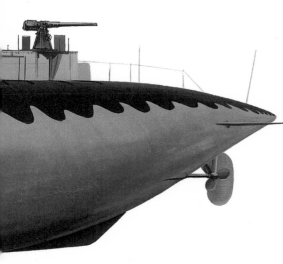

The 'S' class was too small for protected overseas work, however, and to provide this capability for its worldwide commitments, the Royal Navy developed the larger but otherwise similar 'T' class, which had no fewer than ten 21in (533mm) torpedo tubes located as eight in the bows (including two in the bulbous bow casing) and two amidships in the casing.

Throughout this period of considerable technical improvement in the design and construction of submarines, Germany had been prohibited by the terms of the Treaty of Versailles from any involvement in submarine development. Determined not to fall behind, however, the German authorities established a clandestine method of keeping abreast of developments, primarily through the agency of design offices in neutral countries such as the Netherlands, Spain and the USSR, where submarines were designed and built for local use as well as for the export market.

When the Nazi party came to power in 1933, therefore, Germany lacked submarines but was more or less conversant with the latest submarine designs. Thus, when it was decided in 1934 to resume the construction of submarines in Germany, considerable expertise was available for the rapid creation of an indigenous design capability. At this time, the German navy was considering five basic types of boat, in the forms of a coastal boat with a displacement of up to 500 tons, a coastal minelayer also with a displacement of up to 500 tons, a sea-going boat with a displacement of up to 750 tons, an ocean-going boat with a displacement of 1,000 tons, and a submarine cruiser with a displacement of 1,500 tons. The origins of the sea-going type were found in the *Gür*, which had been designed as the 'Type IA'

45

The 'Type A' midget submarine had a submerged displacement of 46 tons, a length of 78ft 6in (23.9m), a single-shaft propulsion arrangement with a 600hp (447kW) electric motor for surfaced and submerged speeds of 23 and 19 knots respectively, a range of only 80 miles (129km), a crew of two, and an armament of two 18in (457mm) tubes each carrying a single torpedo.

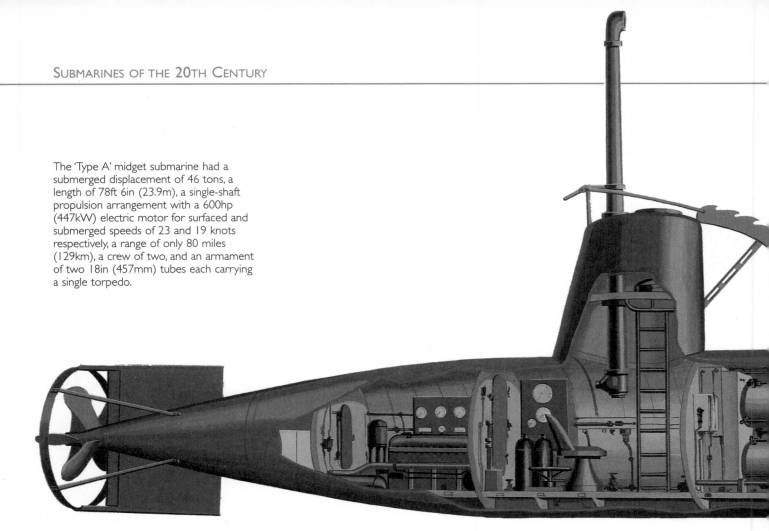

class by a German team and built in Spain for Turkey in the earlier 1930s, and which also formed the basis of the Soviet 'Stalinets' class, while three of the other types were based more loosely on the best German designs of World War I: the 'Type II' coastal type was modelled on the 'UB II' class, the 'Type VII' sea-going type was based on the 'UB III' class with a number of improvements developed for the Finnish 'Vetehinen' class, and the 'Type IX' ocean-going type was derived from the 'UE II' class. All three types proved successful, and were therefore built in large numbers through a succession of steadily improved subvariants which incorporated the lessons learned from their predecessors.

The most important of the types developed before the outbreak of World War II in September 1939 was possibly the 'Type VIIB', which was a slightly enlarged version of the 'Type VIIA' with higher-powered diesel engines and modified saddle tanks for improved seaworthiness; enlarged bunkerage ensured increased range despite the higher surfaced speed. The type had surfaced and submerged displacements of 753 and 857 tons respectively, a length of 218ft 3in (66.52m) and beam of 20ft 3in (6.17m), a two-shaft propulsion arrangement with 2,800hp (2,088kW) diesel engines and 750hp (559kW) electric engines for surfaced and submerged speeds of 17.25 and 8 knots respectively, surfaced and submerged ranges of 6,500 and 80 miles (10,460 and 129km) respectively at speeds of 12 and 4 knots, a crew of 44, and an armament of five 21in (533mm) tubes (four in the bows and one in the stern) for 12 torpedoes or 14 mines, plus one 3.465in (88mm) deck gun supplemented by one 20mm cannon for anti-aircraft use. The 'Type VII' submarine was easy to build and, by submarine standards, was decidedly useful but was not ideally suited to the type of submarine operations that Germany launched in World War II as its surfaced range was somewhat

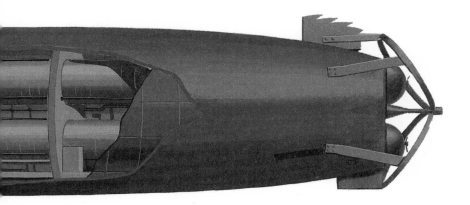

'Type A' midget submarine

DESIGNED to operate within the context of the Combined Fleet for the decisive conflict thought inevitable with the US Navy's Pacific Fleet in a war between Japan and the USA, the 'Type A' midget submarine was intended to penetrate American harbours and cripple major warships lying at anchor in them. The prototype boats were based on the shape of the torpedo, and therefore possessed no conning tower, and had all-electric propulsion based on a large battery capacity that had to be charged by a parent vessel as the boats themselves carried no charging equipment. The lack of a conning tower was deemed impractical for purposes of surfaced navigation, and the following *Ha 1* and *Ha 2* pre-production boats thus introduced a conning tower and a superimposed pair of torpedo tubes in the bows. These two boats were completed by Kure Navy Yard in 1936, and their success in trials led to the placement of orders for 41 production boats to be delivered by Ourazaki for deployment on adapted seaplane carriers such as the *Chitose*, *Chiyoda* and *Mizuho*, which carried out their first midget submarine trials in 1941; the 'Type C1' class attack submarine could also carry one 'Type A' midget boat on the deck casing abaft the conning tower. The initial 41 boats were complemented from 1942 by another 15 generally similar craft, which like their surviving predecessors were generally operated in the training and harbour defence roles as early operations with the first boats had revealed that lack of range was an intractable tactical limitation. The boats completed before the outbreak of war in December 1941 generally had free-flooding torpedo tubes, while those completed later had bow caps for the tubes as well as other improvements such as propeller guards, net cutters and jumper wires to facilitate penetration through anti-submarine nets.

limited and its internal volume too small for protracted patrols: such operations demanded that virtually every part of the space inside the submarine had to be packed with additional food and spare equipment, which had an adverse effect on habitability and therefore long-term operational capability.

It is worth digressing at this point to consider the nature of the anti-submarine capability that had been evolved in the period between the world wars. The most important single element of this capability was the ASDIC system that could both detect and secure the bearing and range of a submerged submarine. Named after the Allied Submarine Devices Investigation Committee that had been created in 1918 to look into the matter of combating German submarines, ASDIC (or more generally Asdic) was based on a sonic pulse transmitted through the water to create an echo that bounced off the target submarine, the bearing of the echo's maximum return being the bearing of the target, and the time between the despatch of the pulse and the receipt of the echo being used to calculate range. This was of major importance in the battle against the submarine, and by the outbreak of World War II some 200 British escort warships had been fitted with the device, which was thought to provide a decisive edge over the submarine. Asdic, or sonar (sound navigation and ranging) as it was known to the Americans, was certainly a vital element in the anti-submarine arsenal, but was dangerously over-emphasised in British tactical thinking in the period before the World War II.

Too few vessels were fitted with the equipment, and peacetime trials had failed to reveal the full extent of Asdic's limitations, especially against a surfaced submarine or when the Asdic-equipped warship passed over a submerged submarine, which allowed submarine captains to develop the tactic of changing course, speed and depth as the warship arrived overhead to attack with its depth charges, which could only be fired laterally and dropped over the stern on the target submarine's anticipated position.

At the start of World War II, the German navy had 56 operational submarines and another five were in the final stages of construction. This was a small number with which to start operations (the German navy had planned on the basis of a later war, as indicated by Germany's Nazi leadership), and 40 were already on their war stations off the UK, sinking the liner *Athenia* on the first day of hostilities despite Hitler's instructions that such targets were not to be attacked for fear of antagonising neutral opinion. Even so, the German submarine captains were very careful in their selection of targets, and up to the time of Germany's major assault in the west, which started in May 1940, the Germans had sunk only 199 merchant ships and in the process had lost 18 of their own submarines. The Germans had also enjoyed a considerable measure of success against warships, sinking the aircraft-carrier *Courageous* and the elderly battleship *Royal Oak* amongst others. Although in real terms it was the loss of the aircraft-carrier that was more important than the sinking of the battleship in its protected anchorage in Scapa Flow, it was the loss of the battleship that had the more profound effect on the British, who were still battleship- rather than carrier-minded and now felt compelled to relocate their major surface units to a number of secondary bases.

During this period the British, who had only 38 submarines available in home waters at the beginning of the war, used their boats in the manner that had become standard in the latter part of World War I, which was mainly reconnaissance off German ports to warn of any movement by Germany's major surface units. This activity was counterproductive, for the Germans were undertaking little in the way of such movements and were able to deal fairly harshly with the British submarines.

Built by Kure Navy Yard and completed in March 1927, the *I-53* was renumbered as the *I-153* in May 1942. The boat was one of the few Japanese submarines to survive World War II, and after the Japanese surrender was scrapped in 1946. The submarine is seen here running its Hiroshima Bay trials during 1927 in standard 'Type KD3A' class submarine cruiser configuration with surfaced and submerged displacements of 1,800 and 2,300 tons respectively, a length of 328ft 1in (100.0m), a two-shaft propulsion arrangement with 6,800hp (5,070kW) diesel engines and 1,800hp (1,342kW) electric motors for surfaced and submerged speeds of 20 and 8 knots, and an armament of eight 21in (533mm) tubes in the bows for 16 torpedoes plus one 4.7in (120mm) deck gun.

The oldest class of British submarines to see active service in World War II, the 'O' class comprised nine boats delivered in a three-boat first group and a six-boat second group with greater displacement and power. The first group, completed in 1926, lost one boat during the war and had its two survivors scrapped in 1945, while the second group, completed in 1928, lost four of its number during the war leaving two boats for disposal at Durban in 1946 (one scrapped and the other scuttled). Seen here leaving Valetta harbour in Malta is the first group's Otway, which was allocated to the Royal Australian Navy in 1927. The boat had surfaced and submerged displacements of 1,350 and 1,870 tons respectively, a length of 275ft 0in (83.82m), a two-shaft propulsion arrangement with 3,000hp (2,237kW) diesel engines and 1,350hp (1,007kW) electric motors for surfaced and submerged speeds of 15.5 and 9 knots respectively, a crew of 54, and an armament of eight 21in (533mm) torpedo tubes (six in the bows and two in the stern) and one 4in (102mm) gun.

The first opportunity for the British boats to shine came with the German invasion of Norway in April 1940, when British boats (supplemented by the French *Rubis*) started to lay major minefields off the Norwegian coast and to attack German shipping taking German troops into Norway and then supplying them during the following weeks: the *Spearfish* damaged the pocket battleship *Lützow* and the *Clyde* seriously hurt the battle-cruiser *Gneisenau*, and, in combination with other successes by the British surface and submarine forces during this period, hit the German navy so hard that it lacked the strength for the invasion of the UK planned for later in the same year.

Part of this success was attributable to the effectiveness of British torpedoes at this time: these impact-fused weapons proved generally successful while the Germans' theoretically more capable magnetically fused weapons were revealing great unreliability: the object of the magnetically fused torpedo was to detonate as the weapon passed under the keel of the target, thereby breaking the target's back rather than merely blowing a hole in the side as was the general result of an impact-fused detonation. In 30 attacks during the spring of 1940, 29 German torpedoes failed and the only successful detonation sank the submarine *Thistle*.

In June 1940, the whole tenor of the war changed with the defeat of France, and Italy's entry into the war on the side of Germany. The Royal Navy, now without French support, had thus to bear the whole burden of the naval war against an opponent whose strength had been considerably enlarged. Moreover, the German submarines were now relishing the prospect of operating from captured French bases with direct access to the South-Western Approaches and the North Atlantic, rather than from German bases that required the boats to pass right around the British Isles.

The Submarine in World War II – The Western Theatre

B Y the end of 1940, no fewer than 12 flotillas of German submarines had moved to the French bases of Brest, La Rochelle, La Pallice, St Nazaire, Lorient and Bordeaux, of which the last also accommodated flotillas comprising a maximum of 27 Italian submarines, which proved generally inferior to their German counterparts as a result of their large conning towers and relatively low surface speed but nevertheless managed to sink nearly one million tons of Allied shipping up to mid-1943 in their primary operational area off the Azores.

The majority of French bases were close to the Germans' most important operational areas, through which the convoys carrying the UK's raw materials, food supplies and oil had to pass. Although the Admiralty had not made the same mistake as in World War I, and had instituted a major convoy system from the outbreak of hostilities, the system and the tactics of its escorts were still in their infancy and therefore offered the German submariners' superb opportunities.

In August 1940, Hitler finally permitted the start of unrestricted submarine warfare, but the German submariners did not at first achieve major successes. The British anti-submarine forces available in the South-Western Approaches had now developed considerable skill, and it was not until they had shifted their operational areas deeper into the Atlantic, mostly out of reach of British aircraft and short-range escorts, that the Germans began to achieve greater successes. This is reflected in the fact that between June and November 1940 the German submarines sank 1,600,000 tons of British shipping, mostly in the second half of the period.

Even so, the Germans realised that they faced a difficult task: the USA had exchanged 50 obsolete destroyers, capable of comparatively speedy conversion into effective anti-submarine vessels, for 99-year leases on British bases in the Caribbean, thereby signalling its intention to support Britain against Germany in the same way as it had in World War I; and the German navy, having been informed that the war would be of short duration, was now faced with an acute shortage of boats for operations in the North Atlantic. The production of new boats was accelerated as much as possible, so that while four new boats were delivered between September and December 1939, 60 more came off the slips between January and December 1940, at a steadily increasing rate that was nonetheless still inadequate to replace losses and allow a major expansion of the submarine campaign at a time when the Germans had suffered the loss of 34 boats. Some improvement in the Germans' position had resulted from the British

Inset: During World War II, the specialised anti-submarine aeroplane became as much of a threat to the German U-boats as the surface warship: this is a 'Type IX' submarine under attack by an aeroplane in June 1942.

reaction to the threat of German invasion after the evacuation from Dunkirk in May and June 1940, when most destroyers had been withdrawn from convoy escort duties, but as they could put only some 30 boats into action at any one time, the Germans were still unable to inflict a decisive blow. Even so, the great submarine 'aces' such as Otto Kretschmer and Günther Prien were able to exploit their skills to the maximum, and each sank more than 200,000 tons of shipping in this period.

The tactic evolved by men such as Kretschmer and Prien was the night attack on the surface: here the submarines could not be detected by the Asdic of the British escorts, and their very low silhouettes were virtually impossible to spot. Kretschmer took the concept to its ultimate limit by penetrating into the heart of the convoy before starting his attack, making it all but impossible for the escorts, which were generally operating in a ring outside the columns of the convoy, to launch a counterattack.

Admiral Karl Dönitz, commanding the submarine arm, took the concept of the night attack a step further by adding it to the 'wolf pack' concept. In this, as many submarines as possible were vectored into position to ambush a convoy discovered by a submarine or a long-range reconnaissance aeroplane: only when a large number of boats had been assembled were they released to make a concentrated night attack, swamping the defences (generally comprising converted trawlers, corvettes and sloops that could not match the 17-knot speed of surfaced submarines) and savaging the convoy in a tactic that was repeated on as many successive nights as possible as long as the pack could keep in contact with the luckless convoy. The nocturnal 'wolf pack' attack system was introduced between October 1940 and March 1941, and proved devastating.

The factors that now most limited the success of the German submarines were their lack of range and their relatively small number of reload torpedoes, and this particularly affected the 'Type VII' and 'Type IX' boats that formed the bulk of the flotillas' strength. A partial remedy was the introduction of the 'Type XIV' or 'milch cow' submarines, which were

Here represented by the *Aeneas* completed in October 1945 after construction by Cammell Laird, the British 'A' class submarine was designed for long-range operations in the Pacific Ocean but was completed too late for service in World War II. The class had surfaced and submerged displacements of 1,120 and 1,620 tons respectively, a length of 281ft 9in (85.88m), a two-shaft propulsion arrangement with 4,300hp (3,206kW) diesel engines and 1,250hp (932kW) electric motors for surfaced and submerged speeds of 18 and 8 knots respectively, a crew of 60, and an armament of no fewer than ten 21in (533mm) torpedo tubes, one 4in (102mm) gun and one 20mm anti-aircraft gun. The torpedo tubes were disposed as six (two external) in the bows and four (two external) in the stern.

Fighting the Submarine

THE standard weapon used the submarine in World Wars I and II was the depth charge, which was basically a weighted steel cylinder filled with high explosive and fitted with a hydrostatic pistol on which the desired detonation depth was set before the weapon was released: on landing in the water, the depth charge sank rapidly and on reaching the set depth was exploded to create an expanding spherical pressure wave designed to cause decisive damage to the target. The skill in using the depth charge lay in determining the target submarine's position, course, speed and depth, for only thus could the necessary depth settings be entered on the depth charges of the fired pattern of weapons to create the three-dimensional concussion with the target in it. This was a remarkably difficult thing to achieve, for on hearing the approaching attacker, the target submarine's commander would almost certainly order changes in his boat's course, speed and depth. In the days when depth charges were the only attack option and Asdic (or sonar) lost the submarine as the attacker passed over him, this gave the submarine commander valuable seconds in which to effect the changes and thus negate the intuition of the attacker's commander. In general, therefore, depth charge attacks were protracted and demanded both skill and endurance from the operating crews charged with loading the launcher equipment (one or more rails dropping depth charges over the stern together with two or more projectors firing depth charges laterally over each quarter) and setting the required detonation depth on the hydrostatic pistols. This situation was radically altered by the development of ahead-throwing weapons such as the initial 'Hedgehog' with its 24 impact-fused small bombs and the later 'Squid' and improved 'Limbo' with their three depth-fused large bombs, all of which were fired over the bows of the attacker against a target still held in the attacker's Asdic (or sonar).

By the middle years of World War II, the attentions of Allied bombers were becoming so devastating to the Germans' submarine bases in France that enormous resources, in terms of manpower and material, had to be expended on the creation of bomb-proof 'U-boat pens' that provided a safe lair for submarines between their sorties into the Atlantic. By 1944, however, even these pens were not immune to the latest British bomb, the 12,000lb (5,443kg) 'Tall Boy' dropped by the Avro Lancaster heavy bomber to reach transonic speed before impacting with its target and penetrating deep into it before the warhead was detonated.

produced in modest numbers to supply submarines at sea: each of these boats carried a cargo of 432 tons of oil fuel and four reload torpedoes. Some 10 of the boats were delivered in 1941 and 1942, and all were sunk as the Allies rightly considered them to be a greater threat than the theoretically more dangerous submarines they supported. Despite the importance of the type, another ten boats were cancelled because of their increasing vulnerability to attack and destruction as they transferred fuel whilst on the surface. The same thinking was responsible for the cancellation of the large 'Type XV' and 'Type XVI' submarines that had been planned.

Meanwhile the British had not been idle, and an early response to the surfaced submarine attack was the adoption of Type 271 radar, which could detect the conning tower of a surfaced submarine at a range of 2.5 miles (4km) and allow the escort commander to launch an attack while the submarine was still out of effective torpedo range of the target convoy. Introduced at almost the same time was 'Huff-Duff', which was the equipment not only to detect the high-frequency radio transmissions of Germans submarines making a convoy contact report, but also of fixing its location to within 440yds (400m).

The combination of these two weapons immediately swayed the balance back toward the British, and another factor that aided the British was their ability to read much of the ciphered German signal traffic. Thus March 1941 was a disaster for the Germans, who achieved some successes but also lost five boats including those of the 'aces' Kretschmer, Prien and Schepke.

In concert with their improved electronic 'weapons', the British were devising and introducing more-capable genuine weapons, including Hawker Hurricane fighters launched on a one-way mission from adapted merchant ships to intercept and destroy German reconnaissance aircraft before ditching in the sea close to a ship that could rescue the pilot. Greater long-term success was promised by two other developments that were not yet ready for service. These were the escort carrier, which was a simple conversion of a medium-sized merchant ship so that each major convoy could be provided with its own fighter and anti-submarine aircraft, and the projector type of weapon that could fire its bombs ahead of the ship against a target submarine still held in the Asdic's beam. The first of these projector weapons, appearing in 1941, was the 'Hedgehog', which was a spigot mortar firing a pattern of 24 small impact-fused bombs each carrying 32lb (14.5kg) of Torpex explosive sufficient to penetrate the hull of any submarine. Further development led to the 1943 appearance of the more powerful 'Squid', which fired three full-sized depth charges each containing 300lb (136kg) of explosive and therefore possessing the ability to cause catastrophic damage with a near miss as well as a direct hit.

In December 1941 the USA entered the war on the Allied side after the Japanese attack on the Hawaiian base of Pearl Harbor and Germany's subsequent declaration of war. This immediately eased the British task as the US Navy was now able to play a more active part than its previous patrolling on the western side of the Atlantic, and as American production facilities were more readily available to meet British needs. In the early part of 1942, therefore, six merchant hulls were converted into escort carriers and, of these, five were delivered to the UK, which had pioneered the escort carrier with great success with the *Audacity* that had proved its worth in 1941 before being sunk after a one-month career.

Named for one of Germany's greatest submarine 'aces' of World War I, Otto Weddigen, whose tiny U-9 had sunk the British armoured cruisers *Hogue*, *Aboukir* and *Cressy* in a single short engagement, this was the German navy's 1st Submarine Flotilla, complete with depot ship, seen at Kiel in 1937.

The 'S' class submarine was one of the most successful British types of World War II, and was built in large numbers between 1932 and 1945.

Paradoxically, the American entry into the war was initially a disaster for what was now the Allied powers, for the US Navy was poorly equipped for the modern anti-submarine role and the US merchant marine offered a large and tempting number of targets for the German submarine arm, which therefore enjoyed one of its 'happy times' during the first six months of 1942, when a force of only 21 boats sank more than 500 American ships, mostly off the eastern seaboard of the USA and in the Caribbean.

The lack of American preparedness for the submarine onslaught, despite its patrolling to the mid-Atlantic point at which the British assumed responsibility, was a result of the US Navy's continued disbelief in the efficacy of the convoy system, and its reliance on the aggressive use of hunter-killer groups of destroyers to search out and destroy German submarines. This hunter-killer tactic proved itself a notably inefficient way to use warships optimised for fleet tasks, especially as the convoys were the best place to find the submarines, and the revelation of this fact persuaded the Americans to adopt a different strategy. The British had already ordered 50 escort destroyers from American yards, and this slower but more fully optimised anti-submarine type was then adopted by the US Navy, which soon ordered 200 of the ships for its own use. By 1943 the US Navy had more than 1,000 anti-submarine escorts on order.

By this time the position of the Allies in the Atlantic was critical. During 1941 the Germans had sunk 4,328,000 tons of British shipping, of which about half had succumbed to the submarines and the remainder to a combination of mines and attacks by aircraft and surface raiders. In 1942, the German submarines were responsable for more than 6,000,000 tons of the 7,790,000 tons of Allied shipping lost. Moreover, whereas the German submarine force had amounted to 91 boats at the beginning of the year, by December 1942 it totalled 212 operational boats despite the loss of 87 submarines during the course of the year. This boded extremely well for the German war effort, which was now based largely on the need to secure victory in Europe before the Americans could bring their vast industrial and manpower resources to bear on the continent. The Germans calculated that they would have to sink at least 800,000 tons of shipping per month to achieve their object of starving the British into submission and preventing the arrival of substantial US forces, and during 1942 the Allied loss rate ran at 650,000 tons per month. This was an extremely parlous situation for the Allies, and the replacement of the sunk merchant tonnage became of paramount importance. The solution was found in the development of the 'Liberty' and 'Victory' class ships, which were standardised types that could be built quickly and economically, and in the fact that the British escort building programmes were beginning to bear fruit in this period with the delivery of an increasing number of 'River' class frigates and other ships, all equipped with increasingly sophisticated electronic systems to swell the number of German submarine losses.

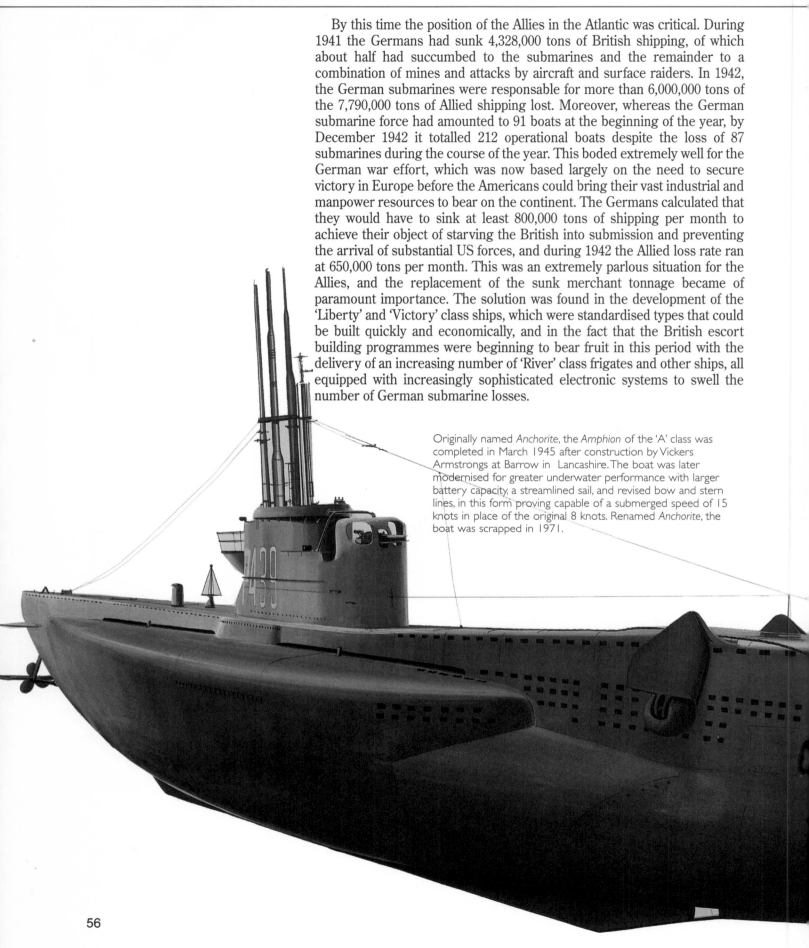

Originally named Anchorite, the Amphion of the 'A' class was completed in March 1945 after construction by Vickers Armstrongs at Barrow in Lancashire. The boat was later modernised for greater underwater performance with larger battery capacity, a streamlined sail, and revised bow and stern lines, in this form proving capable of a submerged speed of 15 knots in place of the original 8 knots. Renamed Anchorite, the boat was scrapped in 1971.

A German chart entitled 'England's Dead' shows the claimed (and indeed generally correct) sinkings of British ships round the British Isles in the period between September 1939 and September 1940.

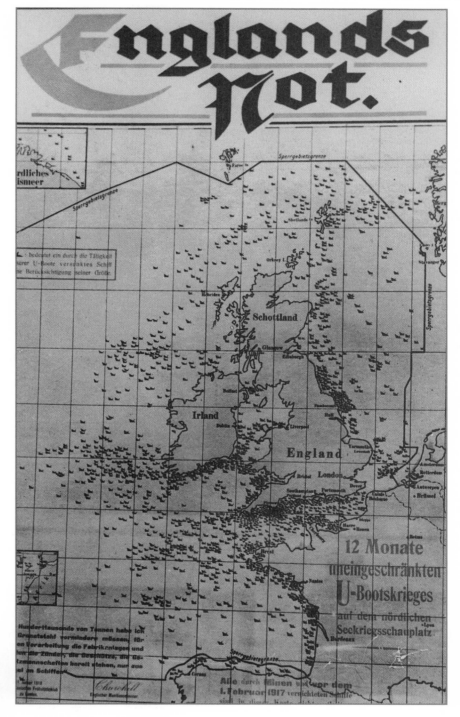

The Allies were still highly vulnerable in the 'mid-Atlantic gap', an area that could not be covered by land-based aircraft operating from the UK, the Azores or the USA. German submarines could operate without the threat of Allied air attack until the situation was redressed by the advent of larger numbers of escort carriers and of very-long-range aircraft such as the Consolidated B-24 Liberator in its specialised maritime patrol versions.

Overestimates of the tonnages its submarines were sinking persuaded the submarine arm's command that the target of 800,000 tons per month was on the verge of attainment, and the campaign against Allied merchant shipping was therefore maintained at as high a pitch as possible. The high command felt that two new developments would finally tip the balance

Seen while being moved to the water after construction at the Howaldtswerke yard at Kiel, the 'Type XVII' submarine was based on the Walther propulsion system and construction was based on the assembly of prefabricated sections to speed the process. These boats, whose high speed was partially offset by their short range and difficult propulsion system, could cover 114 miles (183km) at 20 knots on their Walther geared turbine propulsion system.

decisively in favour of the submarine. These developments involved the acoustically homing torpedo to increase the likelihood of securing a decisive hit, and the radar detector to reduce the likelihood of submarines being caught unawares on the surface by radar-fitted Allied warships (and, increasingly, specialised anti-submarine aircraft that could swoop down for the kill with little or no warning).

The advent of these two new devices coincided more or less with two Allied 'failures'. The first of these was the general withdrawal of American escort forces from the Atlantic in June 1942 for use in the Pacific, which at that time was considered the more dangerous theatre, and the second was the thinning of the surviving merchant convoy escort forces in the Atlantic to provide support for the military convoys preparing for the Allied invasion

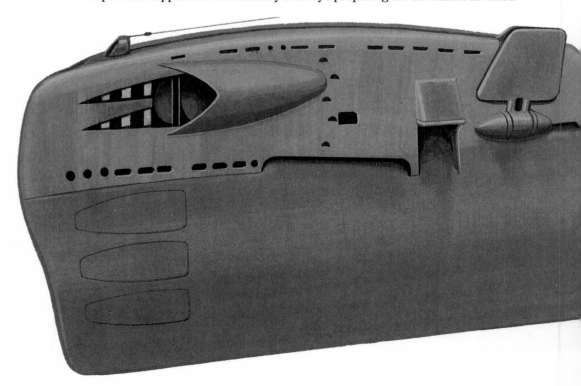

of French North-West Africa scheduled for November 1942. The effect of the German technical developments and Allied diminution was a tilt in the balance toward the Germans that was offset, only partially at first, by the advent of the first Allied support groups.

Made possible by the comparatively large number of new escort vessels that were now coming into service under increasingly experienced commanders, these groups were designed specifically for the hunting and killing of German submarines drawn to the magnet of the convoys and their close escort forces. These escort forces looked after the immediate protection of their convoys, leaving the support groups to operate on a longer leash to detect incoming submarine forces and prosecute their contacts over a protracted period without having to worry about convoy protection.

This meant that by the beginning of 1943, the sides were moderately well balanced and each in a relatively strong position with an increasing number of modern and well-equipped vessels manned by increasingly experienced and determined crews under capable captains. The one significant edge possessed by the Allies, however, was their possession of long-range aircraft fitted with progressively sophisticated radar. Despite this fact, it was the Germans who achieved the first major success of the year when, in March, they used intelligence information to ensure the interception by 39 submarines of 77 ships (52 in a slow convoy and 25 in a fast convoy). In the resulting battle, 21 ships totalling 140,000 tons were sunk for the loss of only three submarines. It was a major German victory, and had rightly come to be regarded as the high point in the German effort in the Battle of the Atlantic. The immediate results of this clash were a further strengthening of the German resolve to crush the UK by destroying the convoy system on which the nation was wholly reliant, and a wavering in the British naval high

The submarines of the 'T' class were among the most successful and widely deployed British boats of World War II, and substantial numbers were built in two main groups. Launched between 1937 and 1941, the 22 boats of the first group had surfaced and submerged displacements of 1,090 and 1,575 tons respectively, a length of 275ft 0in (83.82m), a two-shaft propulsion arrangement with 2,500hp (1,864kW) diesel engines and 1,450hp (1,081kW) electric motors for surfaced and submerged speeds of 15.25 and 9 knots respectively, a crew of 59, and an armament of ten (or eleven in the last seven boats) 21in (533mm) torpedo tubes located as six internal and two external bow tubes plus two (or three in the last seven boats) external stern tubes as well as one 4in (102mm) deck gun. The 30 boats of the second group differed in details such as their two-shaft propulsion arrangement with 2,500hp (1,864kW) diesel engines and 1,450hp (1,081kW) electric motors for surfaced and submerged speeds of 15 and 9 knots respectively, a crew of 65, and an armament of eleven 21in (533mm) torpedo tubes located as six internal and two external bow tubes plus three external stern tubes as well as one 4in (102mm) deck gun and one 20mm anti-aircraft gun.

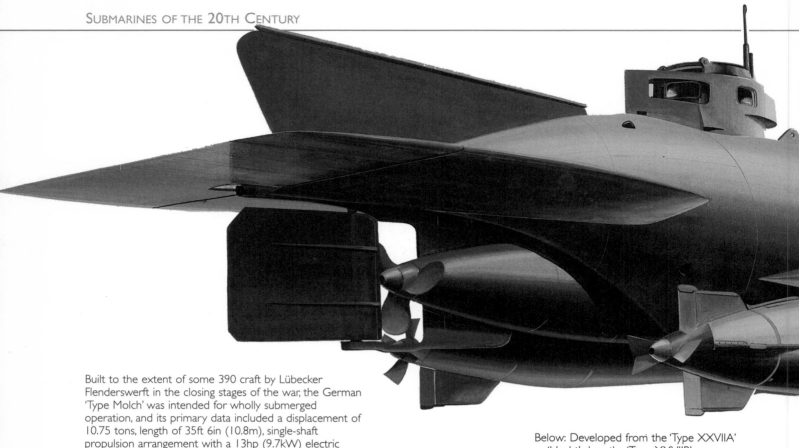

Built to the extent of some 390 craft by Lübecker Flenderswerft in the closing stages of the war, the German 'Type Molch' was intended for wholly submerged operation, and its primary data included a displacement of 10.75 tons, length of 35ft 6in (10.8m), single-shaft propulsion arrangement with a 13hp (9.7kW) electric motor for surfaced and submerged speeds of 5 and0 4.5 knots respectively, crew of one, and an armament of two 21in (533mm) torpedoes carried externally.

Below: Developed from the 'Type XXVIIA' or 'Hecht' class, the 'Type XXVIIB' or 'Seehund' class of midget submarines was built to the extent of some 252 boats with a displacement of 15 tons, length of 39ft 0in (11.9m), single-shaft propulsion arrangement with one 60hp (44.7kW) diesel engine and one 25hp (18.6kW) electric motor for surfaced and submerged speeds of 7.75 and 6 knots respectively, a crew of two, and an armament of two 21in (533mm) torpedoes carried externally.

command, which once again gave serious consideration to the termination of the convoy system in favour of independent sailings until new countermeasures could be introduced.

Fortunately for the Allies, the convoy system was not abandoned, and the March 1943 battle soon proved to be the worst encounter that might be expected with the Germans, principally because the escort carriers and support groups diverted to the Anglo-American landing in French North-West Africa were by now returning to their primary tasks of hunting and killing German submarines. Further impetus was given to the Allied fightback by the American provision of some 60 B-24 Liberator long-range bombers for adaptation as maritime patrol aircraft, and the British introduction of short-range radar for the air-to-surface vessel (ASV) role. This radar was notably important, for it possessed good performance, and was a very significant advantage that could not be detected by the Germans' current generation of radar warning systems. The result was a steep increase in the number of German submarines lost to British air attack, especially as they sortied toward their operational areas on the surface and under the imagined cover of darkness.

The shift in the balance became apparent in May 1943, when another great convoy battle occurred but resulted this time in the loss of only a few merchant ships against the sinking of eight out of 12 attacking submarines as the result of the intervention of aircraft and two support groups. This disaster forced the German submarine command into two errors. Still believing that ample warning of a radar-assisted air attack was provided by its radar warning systems, the command ordered that the submarines

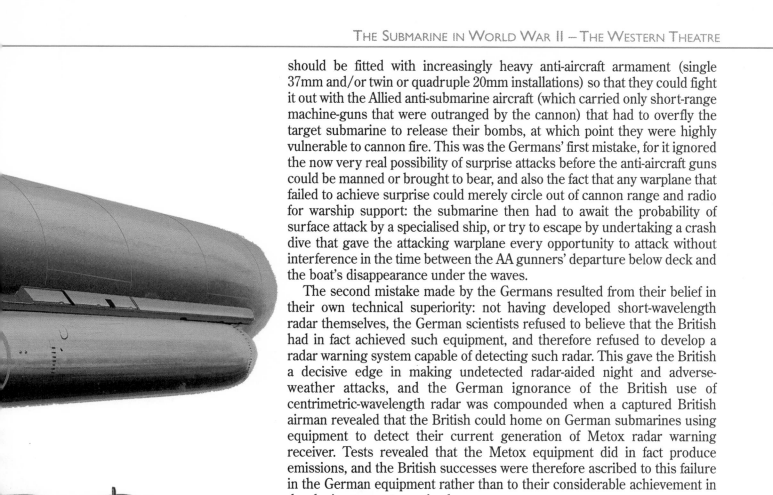

should be fitted with increasingly heavy anti-aircraft armament (single 37mm and/or twin or quadruple 20mm installations) so that they could fight it out with the Allied anti-submarine aircraft (which carried only short-range machine-guns that were outranged by the cannon) that had to overfly the target submarine to release their bombs, at which point they were highly vulnerable to cannon fire. This was the Germans' first mistake, for it ignored the now very real possibility of surprise attacks before the anti-aircraft guns could be manned or brought to bear, and also the fact that any warplane that failed to achieve surprise could merely circle out of cannon range and radio for warship support: the submarine then had to await the probability of surface attack by a specialised ship, or try to escape by undertaking a crash dive that gave the attacking warplane every opportunity to attack without interference in the time between the AA gunners' departure below deck and the boat's disappearance under the waves.

The second mistake made by the Germans resulted from their belief in their own technical superiority: not having developed short-wavelength radar themselves, the German scientists refused to believe that the British had in fact achieved such equipment, and therefore refused to develop a radar warning system capable of detecting such radar. This gave the British a decisive edge in making undetected radar-aided night and adverse-weather attacks, and the German ignorance of the British use of centrimetric-wavelength radar was compounded when a captured British airman revealed that the British could home on German submarines using equipment to detect their current generation of Metox radar warning receiver. Tests revealed that the Metox equipment did in fact produce emissions, and the British successes were therefore ascribed to this failure in the German equipment rather than to their considerable achievement in developing a new type of radar.

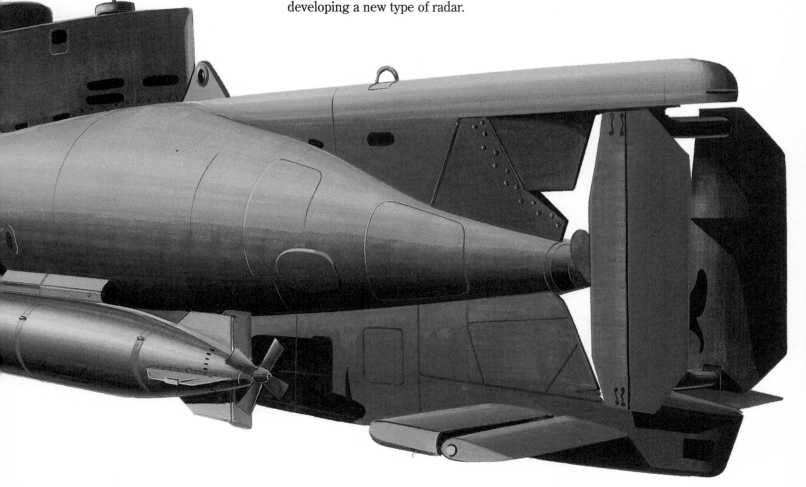

The effect of these two German errors combined with the development of anti-submarine warships and techniques by the British and Canadians, who were responsible for 98 per cent of the oceanic escort work, to shift the balance of the war against the Germans. In April 1943, the Germans had sunk 245,000 tons for the loss of 15 submarines, but in May the trend was reversed by the sinking of 165,000 tons for the loss of 40 submarines, and in the following two months the trend was continued by the sinking of 18,000 tons for the loss of 17 submarines during June and by the sinking of 123,000 tons for the loss of 37 submarines during July. Having been certain just a few months earlier that victory was just around the corner, Dönitz was now forced to concede that his boats had been defeated, and he called a temporary halt to the German offensive until better submarines and new weapons were available.

The devices now adopted as standard features for Germany's new submarines, and as retrofits whenever possible on existing boats, included the *Schnorchel* device to allow the submarine to replenish its air supply and run its battery-charging diesel(s) while operating just under the surface, the Pillenwerfer Asdic-spoofing chemical compound that could be fired into the water off the submarine, and the coating of periscopes and even the hull in

Built by Vickers Armstrongs at Barrow during 1942 and 1943, the six midget submarines of the British 'X' class were intended for service in home waters, and were complemented by 12 generally similar 'XE' class craft built in 1944 and 1945 by Markham of Chesterfield and Marshall of Gainsborough for service in the Far East with equipment for service in a hotter climate.

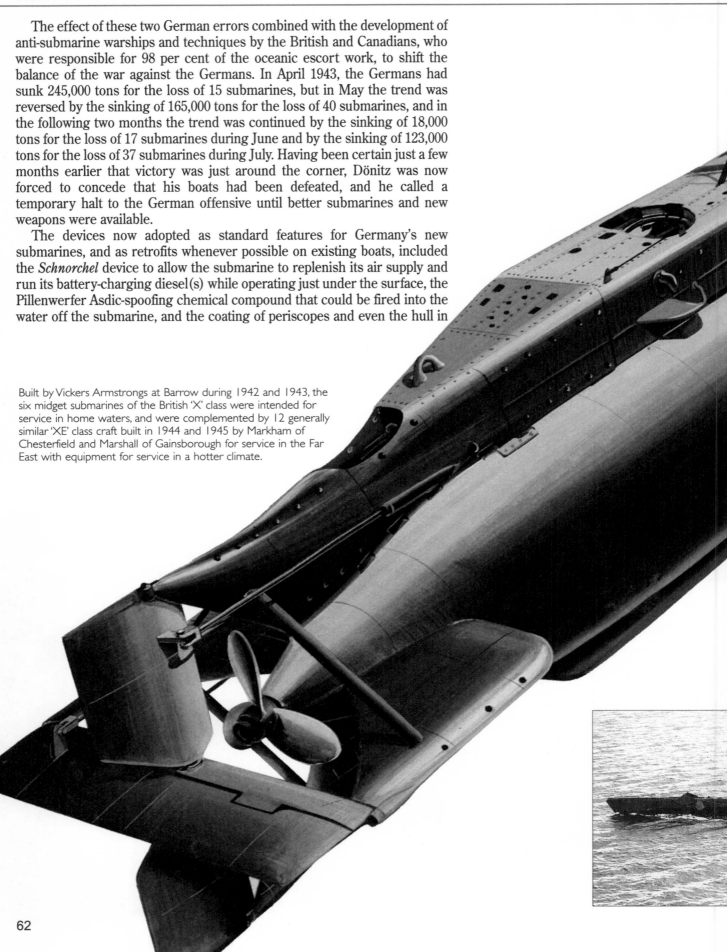

rubberised compounds which would, it was hoped, absorb rather than reflect electro-magnetic and acoustic energy.

These were considered to be palliatives at best, and the greatest hopes were built round the successful development and production of the Walther propulsion system, which was basically a closed-cycle turbine system which burned a mix of diesel oil and concentrated hydrogen peroxide to provide high power levels independent of atmospheric oxygen. This opened the possibility of true submarine rather than submersible operations, freeing the submarine from the chance of detection by radar and offering, when the system was installed in a streamlined hull, submerged speeds at least equal to surfaced speeds. The Walther propulsion system had first been tested in 1940, and made its production debut with the 'Type XVIIA' coastal submarines, of which four were completed in 1943 with a propulsion arrangement that geared two Walther turbine systems to one shaft for a submerged speed of 26 knots of 5,000hp (3,728kW), which was by far the highest underwater speed attained by any submarine up to that time. This type of surface-independent performance opened up the possibility of a totally revised capability against Allied convoys, so rapid production became the order of the day and designers revised the 'Type XVIIA' design into the 'Type XVIIB' and 'Type XVIIG' designs with only one Walther turbine for the still remarkable submerged speed of 21.5 knots on 2,500hp (1,864kW).

The problem for Germany, however, was the same as that presented by many of the country's other very advanced weapons introduced in this and later stages of World War II: firstly, in terms of money, time and resources, they were extremely expensive to develop, and secondly, they were pressed into production before all their problems had been eliminated, in an effort to stave off the defeat made that much more likely by the virtual nonexistence of Germany's long-term military planning and the frequent foolishness of its political leadership. So far as the Walther-powered submarines were concerned, the main problems that had not yet been overcome were the production and storage of the concentrated hydrogen peroxide oxidant, which was known as Ingolin: this was expensive to manufacture (about eight times as much as diesel oil), and for storage required exceptional cleanliness to prevent rapid decomposition and spontaneous combustion. Ingolin was also consumed at a prodigious rate by the Walther turbine: the 'Type XVIIB' submarine carried 55 tons of Ingolin, which provided a range of 114 miles (183km) at a speed of 20 knots. The submarine also possessed a secondary diesel and electric propulsion arrangement rated at 210 and 77hp (156.5 and 57.4kW) respectively for surfaced and submerged speeds of 8.5 and 5 knots, and surfaced and submerged ranges of 3,000 and 40 miles (4,828 and 64km).

These difficulties made the large-scale production and deployment of Walther-powered submarines problematic, a fact fully appreciated by Dönitz, who in July 1943 advised Hitler that it would be better to concentrate on an interim type known as the 'Electro' boat that could bridge the gap between the standard *Schnorchel*-equipped submarines and the planned Walther-powered boats. The first of this interim series was the 'Type XXI' class, which was an ocean-going submarine of the conventionally powered type with a number of improved features designed to offset the several advantages that the Allies had recently come to enjoy. The improved features were a very well-streamlined hull and conning tower to reduce submerged drag, and trebled battery capacity for greater underwater endurance at higher speed.

Such a development had been conceptually available for some time, and the availability of submarines of this type in substantial numbers during

Intended mainly for service in the Mediterranean, the 'U' class was built to the extent of 49 boats between 1937 and 1943. The boats were produced in two subclasses as the 15 boats of the first group and the 34 boats of the second group with very slightly greater length and displacement. There followed the similar 'V' class of 34 boats built in 1943 and 1944. Seen here is the 'V' class *Upshot*, which was completed in 1944 after construction by Vickers Armstrongs at Barrow.

1944 would have given the Germans enormous tactical advantages. The submarine 'Type XXI' class design had surfaced and submerged displacements of 1,621 and 1,819 tons, a crew of 57, a propulsion arrangement that combined two 2,000hp (1,491kW) diesel engines and 2,500hp (1,865kW) electric motors for surfaced and submerged speeds of 15.5 and 16 knots, surfaced and submerged ranges of 11,150 and 285 miles (17,945 and 460km) respectively at speeds of 12 and 6 knots, and an armament of six 21in (533mm) tubes in the bows for 23 torpedoes (or 12 torpedoes and 12 mines) complemented by four 30mm anti-aircraft cannon in two remotely controlled twin mountings faired into the front and rear upper corners of the conning tower. Other major improvements were all-welded construction from eight prefabricated sections, an upgraded *Schnorchel* system that allowed unlimited submerged running of the diesels for a speed of 12 knots, provision of two 113hp (84.25kW) creeper electric motors for silent running at a maximum of 5 knots, and a powered torpedo reload system to speed this all-important process and allow the implementation of saturation attacks.

Dönitz assured Hitler that the existing production system could start deliveries of these improved submarines from November 1944, but the German leader was insistent that earlier deliveries would be possible if the Nazi production system took over, and as a result production of the 'Type XXI' was entrusted to a system that ran construction of the obsolete 'Type VIIC' class in parallel with that of the magnificent 'Type XXI', whose building was thus undertaken by teams that combined one-third of skilled personnel with two-thirds of unskilled labour including old men, women and even children not required for conscription into the armed forces.

This insanely run system could not succeed, however, for the German air force had overriding priority for many of the required strategic materials, and the German army had priority for the manpower which would have been required to crew the new submarines, whose production Dönitz

Operated in home, Mediterranean and Far Eastern waters, the 'T' class was built to the extent of 52 boats between 1937 and 1944. The boats were completed in two subclasses as the 22 boats of the first group and the 30 boats of the second group with minor improvements. The boat illustrated is the *Thunderbolt*, built by Cammell Laird in 1938 and initially commissioned as the *Thetis*. The boat sank in Liverpool Bay during June 1939 and was renamed after being salvaged and refurbished, but was sunk by Italian warships in March 1943.

A member of the early 'Type VIIA' class of sea-going submarines, the *U-35* was launched in September 1936 and sunk by three British destroyers off the Shetland Islands in November 1939.

estimated at 27 boats per month in the second half of 1943 rising to 30 boats per month in 1945. In the event, additional manpower was later provided by transfers from the army and air force, but the shortages of steel required for submarine construction could never be overcome.

The effect of all these changes was a diminution of the submarine arm's overall efficiency and determination, and even the availability of the *Schnorchel* was in many ways detrimental, for its ability to provide comparatively safe underwater progress removed the chance for the high-speed surface manoeuvring that had often given the German submarines an edge in their battles with convoys and their escorts. Further Allied developments also resulted in radar that could detect a *Schnorchel* in smooth conditions, and the 'Foxer' towed decoy for acoustic homing torpedoes. From the middle of 1943 the invasion of Italy by the Allies and then their slow progress northward along the peninsula gradually deprived the Germans of the bases they needed for submarine operations in the eastern Mediterranean, and the invasions of north-west and southern France in July and August 1944 removed the bases that had provided the strongpoints for German operations in the Atlantic and western Mediterranean respectively.

The Mediterranean became an Allied 'lake' from this time forward, and in northern waters the submarines were forced back to their original German bases, which meant that they had once again to undertake the long and dangerous trip round the north of Scotland before they could reach their operational areas or return home. Thus the only area in which the German submarines continued to enjoy a measure of success was that offered by the Norwegian Sea and Arctic Ocean, where they encountered the Allied convoys plying the route to the ports of the northern USSR.

The Germans were therefore compelled to turn their attention to a number of midget submarine classes that could only operate in sheltered waters, but although built in large numbers, these 'Molch', 'Hecht', 'Seehund', 'Biber', 'Marder' and 'Neger' types proved almost wholly ineffective in real terms. The 'Type XXIII' coastal and 'Type XXI' ocean submarines with Walther propulsion began finally to reach service from the last weeks of 1945, but despite their technical sophistication, became available too little and too late to have any effect on the final outcome of the submarine war.

Thus the German submarine effort, which had been so close to success in May 1943, ended in total decline during May 1945, when the German

Built to the extent of four boats in 1938, the Italian 'Brin' class had a displacement of 1,000 tons, surfaced and submerged speeds of 17.4 and 8.7 knots respectively, and an armament of eight 21in (533mm) torpedo tubes and one 3.9in (100mm) deck gun. Two of the boats were transferred to the Spanish Nationalist navy in 1938-39 and replaced by two similar submarines.

surrender at the end of World War II compelled all submarines at sea to surface, fly a black flag, and then search out the Allied warships that would accept their surrender. The surrendered submarines were then concentrated at Lisahally in Northern Ireland, just as they had been at Harwich in 1919, and were then taken for disposal.

This is not the whole story of the submarine war in the west, however, for mention should also be made of the British midget submarine effort in northern waters, and of the exploits of British and Italian 'chariots' and submarines in the Mediterranean.

Although they were beaten into the field by the Italians and Japanese, the British emerged from World War II as the most successful protagonists of the midget submarine, which was built in two closely related forms for European and Far Eastern operational service. The European type, of which six were built in 1942-43 and complemented by six generally similar but less well-equipped training boats, had a crew of four, surfaced and submerged displacements of 37 and 40 tons respectively, a propulsion arrangement of one 42hp (31.3kW) diesel engine and one 30hp (22.4kW) electric motor for surfaced and submerged speeds of 6.5 and 5.5 knots respectively, and an armament comprising two side cargoes each containing 4,480lb (2,032kg) of explosive for release under the target and subsequent detonation by a time fuse.

The 12 boats built for Far Eastern service in 1944-45 were quite similar except for their slightly increased length, which resulted in surfaced and submerged displacements of 30 and 34 tons respectively with a crew of four or five, and surfaced and submerged speeds of 6.5 and 6 knots respectively. Other changes were air-conditioning, an airlock so that a diver could exit the boat and attach limpet mines to the target, and spring-loaded legs that helped to stabilise the boat on the seabed.

The most important raids and missions undertaken by these important little craft included the attack on the German battleship *Tirpitz* in a Norwegian fjord during September 1944, reconnaissance of the Normandy beaches and service as navigation markers during the invasion over these beaches in June 1944, and attacks on Japanese cruisers in Singapore harbour in 1945.

The 'Saphir' class of French submarine minelayers, here represented by the *Rubis* that made 22 minelaying sorties in the North and Norwegian Seas before being laid up in January 1945, was notably successful.

Following the Italian lead, the British also developed the 'chariot' or human torpedo, which was an evolution of the torpedo with provision for a crew of two to ride on the weapon, penetrate to the target and attach the warhead with cables, and then depart before the timed detonation of the warhead. Efforts were made to employ the 'chariot' around Norway, but the water was too cold for the exposed crewmen, and the type was therefore employed more profitably in the Mediterranean, where craft of this type sank the Italian cruisers *Bolzano*, *Gorizia* and *Ulpio Traiano*.

The Mediterranean was vital to British war plans, and when Italy entered the war in June 1941, the British immediately feared a major outbreak of German and Italian submarine attack on their naval units and convoy routes all along the Mediterranean. The British were fortunate, however, for the best of the Italian submarines and commanders were despatched through the Strait of Gibraltar to operate in the central Atlantic from a base at Bordeaux, and the Germans decided not to weaken their North Atlantic offensive by diverting boats to the Mediterranean.

This left the British with a relatively free hand to use their own submarines in a highly effective manner for the interception and destruction of Italian shipping, which was moving men, equipment and supplies from Italy to North Africa, where a major land campaign erupted between the British and their imperial allies on the one side, and the Italians and then the Germans on the other. Despite the operational difficulties of the theatre, in which aircraft were seldom far from the scene of any naval activity and could detect a submarine down to about 50ft (15m) depth in virtually all conditions (compared with only periscope depth in the North Sea and 30ft (9m) in the north Atlantic), the British submarines exacted a very high toll from the Italians.

The British submarines initially used in the Mediterranean were the boats of the 'O', 'P' and 'R' classes, which were easy to identify not only because of their comparatively large size but also by the fact that their external bunkers tended to leak oil; despite these factors, the success rate of the boats was high. By May 1941, British submarines operating from Gibraltar, Malta and Alexandria had sunk more than 100,000 tons of Italian shipping, and in the middle months of the year the boats disposed of another 150,000 tons using torpedoes or, whenever possible, their more economical deck guns that were also employed for the shelling of coastal targets such as railway lines and bridges.

The British success rate imposed a very severe strain on the relations between the Italians and Germans, for the latter blamed the former for the fact that wholly inadequate quantities of equipment and supplies reached their joint forces operating in North Africa. It seemed that the British were within an ace of securing a major and relatively bloodless triumph over the Axis naval and land forces operating in the Mediterranean and on its southern shore, but it was at this point that the Germans decided to intervene more forcefully by introducing some of their own submarines into the theatre.

The effects of this change in Axis deployment was rapid: in November 1941, German submarines torpedoed and sank the aircraft carrier *Ark Royal* and battleship *Barham*, and in the following month sank the

Opposite: A 'Type IXC' submarine leaves its base at Kiel in northern Germany for a sortie in the earlier part of World War II. The ocean-going 'Type IX' design was developed from the 'U-81' class of World War I with higher surfaced speed, longer range and provision for a larger number of reload torpedoes.

cruiser *Galatea*. Further misery was added by the activities of Italian human torpedoes; in December 1941 two of these craft penetrated into Alexandria harbour and succeeded in inflicting severe damage on the battleships *Queen Elizabeth* and *Valiant*.

The events of 1941 in the Mediterranean coincided with the start of the Japanese onslaught through the Pacific and into South-East Asia, and an immediate British response was the despatch to this theatre of most of the surviving surface warships from the Mediterranean, leaving the initiative in the Mediterranean to the Germans and Italians. British strength in the theatre now rested almost entirely with the surviving submarines, which continued to wreak havoc on Axis supply convoys and occasional surface warships, despite the fact that submarine activities were severely hampered by the large number of German warplanes now operating over the Mediterranean. Even so, the British boats achieved wonders not only in their primary offensive role, but also in the increasingly important secondary task of running essential supplies into Malta, which was now under tight Axis blockade. By the middle of 1942, the submarines had run some 65,000 tons of fuel, food, equipment and medical supplies in to the island. Thereafter the situation eased as the Axis forces in North Africa finally went over to the strategic defensive after September 1942 and were defeated in May 1943.

Only one of the 'L'Aurore' class of French sea-going submarines, of which 15 had been ordered in 1938, was completed before World War II. The Germans took over three incomplete boats and actually finished only one of them, and several of the others were completed after the war to an improved standard. The baseline configuration included surfaced and submerged displacements of 893 and 1,170 tons respectively, a length of 241ft 3in (73.50m), a two-shaft propulsion arrangement with 3,000hp (2,237kW) diesel engines and 1,400hp (1,044kW) electric motors for surfaced and submerged speeds of 14.5 and 9 knots respectively, a crew of 44, and an armament of nine 21.7in (550mm) torpedo tubes and one 3.9in (100mm) deck gun.

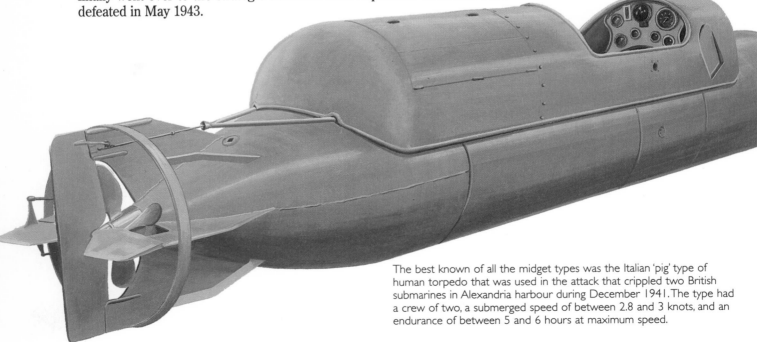

The best known of all the midget types was the Italian 'pig' type of human torpedo that was used in the attack that crippled two British submarines in Alexandria harbour during December 1941. The type had a crew of two, a submerged speed of between 2.8 and 3 knots, and an endurance of between 5 and 6 hours at maximum speed.

The Submarine in World War II – The Eastern Theatre

Japanese thinking in the 1920s and 1930s about the task of the submarine in a future war with the USA in the Pacific Ocean emphasised the laying of major submarine traps into which the US Pacific Fleet could be lured. This demanded submarines large and powerful enough to make long passages on the surface at high speed, the installation of a large battery of torpedo tubes, the carriage of a sizeable number of reload torpedoes and, in an increasing number of the boats, provision for a reconnaissance floatplane carried in a watertight hangar outside the pressure hull.

WHEN Japan entered World War II in December 1941 with its virtually simultaneous attacks on the Americans in Hawaii and the Philippines and on the British in Hong Kong and Malaya, is primary blow was directed against the ships of the US Pacific Fleet in Pearl Harbor. This attack wrought such devastation on the Pacific Fleet's primary surface warships in the theatre that the Americans were forced to revise their strategic thinking to capitalise on their only surviving major assets, namely three large aircraft carriers and a substantial number of the 113 submarines possessed by the US Navy at this time. Unfortunately for the Americans, however, 64 of these were obsolete boats built in World War I and therefore capable of undertaking only training work with a limited degree of operational capability in coastal waters, and nine others were large submarine cruisers whose mechanical unreliability made them ill-suited to

Pacific operations. This left the Americans with 40 modern boats, although the situation was not as bad as this limited total would suggest, for the construction of another 73 submarines had already been authorised, and of these, 32 were currently under construction. Given the fact that the Americans were disposed to leave operations in the Atlantic, where there were few German and Italian targets for submarine attack, this meant that the considerable majority of these new boats were earmarked for the Pacific Fleet.

The number of yards capable of building submarines had declined to three during the period between the world wars, but this number was rapidly doubled as two commercial builders and one navy yard developed submarine-building capability, and deliveries of diesel engines and/or electric motors was assured by the general strength of American industry, which could deliver the required engines and motors without any major difficulty.

With the Pacific clearly the theatre for which the submarines would be required, it was possible to standardise a number of features for the new boats, which were required to possess good habitability, considerable surface range, and volume for a large number of reload torpedoes. This was a philosophy which followed that of the 1920s and 1930s to produce the 10 boats of the 'P' class launched between 1935 and 1937, the 16 boats of the 'S' class launched between 1937 and 1939, and the 12 boats of the 'T' class launched between 1939 and 1941. The last of these classes included the *Tautog*, which was the most successful American submarine of World War II with a record that included the sinking of no fewer than 26 Japanese ships, and its general specification included a crew of 85, a submerged displacement of 2,370 tons, a propulsion arrangement that paired two

The Japanese submarine which sank the American aircraft carrier *Yorktown* during the Battle of Midway in the summer of 1942, the I-68 was the lead boat of the eight-strong 'Type KD6' class of ocean-going submarines. Built by Kure Navy Yard and completed in July 1934, the submarine was torpedoed and sunk by the American submarine *Scamp* in July 1943. The basic details of the 'Type KD6' class included surfaced and submerged displacements of 1,785 and 2,440 tons respectively, a length of 343ft 6in (104.7m), a two-shaft propulsion arrangement with 9,000hp (6,710kW) diesel engines and 1,800hp (1,342kW) electric motors for surfaced and submerged speeds of 23 and 8.25 knots respectively, a range of 14,000 miles (22,530 km) at 10 knots surfaced, and an armament of six 21in (533mm) tubes for 14 torpedoes, and one 3.9in (100mm) deck gun supplemented in later boats by one 4.7in (120mm) deck gun.

2,700hp (2,013kW) diesel engines and two 1,370hp (1,021.5kW) electric motors for surfaced and submerged speeds of 20 and 8.75 knots, an armament of ten 21in (533mm) tubes (six bow and four stern) for 24 torpedoes complemented by one 5in (127mm) gun and four machine-guns.

Experience with the ocean-going submarines of modern design allowed the creation of a basically standardised design for large-scale production from a time early in 1941. This design was based on a diesel-electric propulsion arrangement (diesel generators driving electric motors coupled to the two shafts through reduction gearing) and a hull of all-welded construction allowing a maximum diving depth of 300ft (91m), and was produced in three very closely related subvariants as the 'Gato', 'Balao' and 'Tench' classes (73, 132 and 30 boats respectively), some of the last being completed after the end of the war. The basic design used a double hull (of strengthened construction in the 'Balao' and 'Tench' classes for a maximum diving depth of 400ft/122m) divided into eight watertight compartments, and had four fuel tanks and eight ballast tanks. The primary data for the 'Balao' class included a submerged displacement of 2,425 tons, length of 311ft 9in (95.02m) with a beam of 27ft 3in (8.31m) and draught of 15ft 3in (4.65m), a two-shaft propulsion arrangement that combined General Motors or Fairbanks Morse diesel engines for 5,400hp (4,026kW) and two General Electric or Elliot Motor electric motors for 2,740hp (2,043kW), surfaced and submerged speeds of 20.25 and 8.75 knots respectively, a crew of 85, and an armament of ten 21in (533mm) tubes (six forward and four aft) for 24 torpedoes complemented by one deck gun, which was variously a 5in (127mm) weapon, 4in (102mm) weapon or a 3in (76.2mm) AA weapon supplemented during the course of the war by AA weapons up to 40mm calibre.

The submarine strength eventually offered by the later pre-war boats and the units of the 'Gato', Balao', and 'Tench' classes was very considerable, but was offset in the first two years of the Pacific war by defects in their torpedoes' magnetic fuses, which was basically the same difficulty that had been encountered by the Germans earlier in the war.

The factor that most characterised the American approach to submarine building in World War II was virtually complete standardisation, which facilitated training and equipment of the boats as well as their production on a production-line basis. The same was certainly not true of the Japanese, who had devoted a considerable part of their pre-war production capacity to several classes of submarine cruisers of the type that seemed to fascinate the Japanese naval high command. What became evident in the late 1940s, however, was the Japanese navy's lack of medium-sized submarines for oceanic duties, and this deficiency was first addressed in 1940 with an order for the first nine of a planned 88 but actual 18 'Type K6' class boats.

For their time, the Japanese 'Type STo' class submarines were the largest boats in the world, and were true ocean-going monsters designed to combine in one hull all the attributes and operational capabilities of the preceding classes as well as the capability to attack and destroy major targets, such as the lock gates in the Panama Canal, with their complement of three high-performance floatplanes. Only three boats were finished, two others being 90 per cent or more complete at the end of World War II, and another 12 boats were cancelled in March 1945. The basic details of this class included surfaced and submerged displacements of 5,223 and 6,560 tons respectively, a length of 400ft 3in (122.0m), a two-shaft propulsion arrangement with 7,700hp (5,741kW) diesel engines and 2,400hp (1,789kW) electric motors for surfaced and submerged speeds of 18.75 and 6.5 knots, a range of 30,000 miles (48,280km) at 16 knots surfaced, a crew of 144, and an armament of eight 21in (533mm) tubes for 20 torpedoes, one 5.5in (140 mm) deck gun, ten 25mm anti-aircraft guns, and three floatplanes.

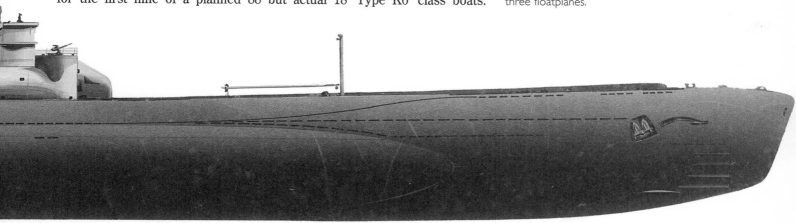

Although rather small and therefore cramped, the boats were considered to be highly successful, and may be likened to the first units of the 'Gato' class in range capability. The basic designs for the 'Type K6' included a crew of 62, surfaced and submerged displacements of 1,115 and 1,447 tons, a length of 264ft 1in (80.5m) with a beam of 22ft 11.5in (7.0m) and a draught of 13ft 1.5in (4.0m), a two-shaft propulsion arrangement that paired diesel engines for 4,200hp (3,131.5kW) and electric motors for 1,200hp (895kW) for surfaced and submerged speeds of 19.75 and 8 knots respectively, surfaced and submerged ranges of 11,000 miles (17,700km) at 12 knots and 45 miles (52km) at 5 knots respectively, and an armament of four 21in (533mm) tubes in the bows for 10 torpedoes and complemented by one 3in (76.2mm) anti-aircraft gun and two 25mm cannon.

In the same year the Japanese ordered the first nine of a planned 27 but actual 18 boats of the 'Type KS' class, which was a somewhat smaller scouting submarine with a submerged displacement of 782 tons and an armament of four 21in (533mm) tubes for eight torpedoes. It is hard to imagine how these small submarines could ever have been of any real utility except for patrol around Japanese-held islands, for their surfaced range was a relatively indifferent 3,500 miles (5,635km) at 12 knots, which was hardly adequate for the type of grandiose oceanic warfare that the Japanese navy was planning.

These two classes, one possessing a genuine ocean-going capability and the other little more than a coastal type, were something of an oddity in Japanese thinking at this time, and in 1941 the Japanese navy returned to the concept of the very large ocean-going submarine with considerable range and endurance, heavy armament and, in most cases, provision for a small reconnaissance/spotter floatplane that could be dismantled for accommodation in a watertight hangar. These classes comprised the planned 14 but actual six units of the 'Type B2' class with a submerged displacement of 3,700 tons and an armament of six 21in (533mm) tubes for 17 torpedoes, the planned 10 but actual three units of the 'Type C2' class with a submerged displacement of 3,564 tons and an armament of eight 21in (533mm) tubes for 20 torpedoes but no seaplane, the single 'Type A2' class unit that was a virtual copy of the three 'Type A1' class boats of 1937 with a submerged displacement of 4,172 tons and an armament of six 21in (533mm) tubes for 18 torpedoes, the planned 32 but actual three units of the 'Type B3' class with a submerged displacement of 3,688 tons and an

This photograph reveals the Japanese submarines *I-402*, *I-36* and *I-47* at their moorings after they had been surrendered to the Americans. All of the boats were scuttled in April 1946. The *I-402* was a 'Type STo' class long-range attack submarine, the I-36 was a 'Type B1' class scouting submarine, and the I-47 was a 'Type C2' class attack submarine.

armament of six 21in (533mm) tubes for 19 torpedoes, and the planned 45 but actual three units of the generally similar 'Type C3' class with a submerged displacement of 3,644 tons and an armament of six 21in (533mm) tubes for 19 torpedoes.

The basic operational thinking that lay behind the design and construction of these classes was the long-cherished desire of the Japanese navy to seek out and destroy the US Navy's Pacific Fleet in a titanic Pacific battle. The large submarines were created within this overall scheme with the object of reconnoitring for the Combined Fleet and picking off any of the American warships on which they could achieve a firing solution. It was also appreciated that the Combined Fleet's surface and underwater units might not be able to bring the Pacific Fleet out to fight, especially after the attack on Pearl Harbor, and to provide an alternative capability to attack the American warships in harbour, the Japanese created a number of midget submarine classes that could be carried by large submarines or seaplane carriers to points off the major American bases and there launched to penetrate the harbour defences and attack the American warships lying at anchor.

The first of these midget submarine designs was the 'Type A' that appeared in 1936 as a development of an experimental boat built two years earlier. The 'Type A' design had a two-man crew, a submerged displacement of 46 tons, a 600hp (447kW) electric motor for surfaced and submerged speeds of 23 and 19 knots respectively, a range of 160 miles (257km) at 6 knots submerged, and an armament of two 18in (457mm) tubes for two torpedoes. Production totalled 41 boats, and after their failure in the Pearl Harbor operation, in which one boat was lost before the main attack was launched, the surviving units were relegated to the harbour defence role.

Further development of the midget submarine concept led in 1942 to the sole 'Type B' class unit that was an improved version of the 'Type A', and the success of this unit led to the construction of 15 'Type C' class units with slightly greater length and displacement to allow the incorporation of a 40hp (29.8kW) diesel engine that provided surfaced propulsion as well as battery recharging capability for surfaced and submerged ranges of 300 and 120 miles (485 and 195km) respectively. The 'Type C' was no more successful in operational terms, however, than the pioneering 'Type A'.

The main encumbrance with Japanese submarines did not tie in their technical features, but rather in the type of employment that was planned for them by the Japanese naval high command. This was beset by the desire for the Combined Fleet to better the Pacific Fleet in open battle, and therefore ignored the operational and strategic possibilities offered by attacks on targets other than warships (which would soon greatly exceed the numbers of American warships in the Pacific), and which were absolutely vital to the prosecution of the long-range amphibious warfare with which the Americans first checked and then rolled back the Japanese after their runaway victories up to the middle of 1942.

Conversely, the Japanese compounded this offensive error with the defensive mistake of thinking that their own shipping would not become a target for American submarine attack. The US Navy fully appreciated, though, that initially unescorted and then only indifferently escorted shipping was Japan's 'Achilles heel': the Japanese war effort was almost wholly reliant on the inward flow of raw materials and oil, and on the outward flow of finished weapons, equipment and men. From the beginning of the war, therefore, the Americans determined to cut the Japanese maritime lines of communication, starving the war industries in the home islands of the wherewithal to make weapons, and cutting off the Japanese

US Submarine Gun Armament in the Pacific

ALTHOUGH both the Americans and the Japanese relied on the torpedo as their principal weapon in the submarine campaign in the Pacific Ocean during World War II, they each appreciated that the torpedo was not a cost-effective weapon for use against smaller targets. The expenditure of such a weapon, of which only a comparatively small number of reloads could be carried even in the larger boats, was therefore avoided when the shell fire of a deck gun would suffice. The standard deck gun carried by American submarines of the 'Balao' and 'Tench' classes was the 25-calibre 5in (127mm) Gun Mk XIII using the same well-proved and readily available ammunition as used by the primary armament of American destroyers and the secondary armament of many larger American warships. On the 'Tench' class as designed, the gun mounting was installed on the after casing abaft the conning tower, and was operated by a two-man crew (elevation and laying numbers) on the mounting with support from a four-man loading crew on the casing. The mounting weighed 5,940lb (2,694kg), and the gun fired a 53lb (24kg) shell to a range of 14,500 yards (13,260m) at an elevation of 40 degrees. The rest of the gun armament for the 'Tench' class, as it was designed, included an anti-aircraft fit of one 40mm and one 20mm guns on the forward and after parts of the lower conning tower structure. Wartime developments, however, often meant that the 'Tench' class boats had two 5in (127mm) guns on the forward and after casings, and two 40mm guns on the conning tower.

island bastions from all effective means of reinforcement and resupply. The threat posed by such a campaign becomes readily apparent from the fact that Japan relied on sea transport for 20 per cent of its food, 24 per cent of its coal, 88 per cent of its iron ore, 90 per cent of its oil, and 100 per cent for items such as rubber, tin and commodities essential for the maintenance of modern industry and transport.

The effect of the American campaign to sever Japan's maritime lines of communication was enormous, and it is arguable that Japan had been

Opposite: In the later stages of World War II, the Japanese placed increasing reliance on suicide weapons to offset the ever-increasing qualitative and quantitative superiority of the Allies' weapons, and in the naval arena this included the 'Kaiten' type of kamikaze submarine. Seen here in the course of a test launch from the obsolete light cruiser Kitakami in February 1945, this is a 'Kaiten I' class submarine based on the design of the Type 93 torpedo. Large numbers of these weapons were produced to a design that included a submerged displacement of 18.33 tons, a length of 48ft 6in (14.8m), a single-shaft propulsion arrangement with one 550hp (410kW) engine for a speed of 30 knots, a range that could be varied between 85,300yds (78,000m) at 12 knots to 25,100yds (22,950m) at 30 knots, a crew of one, and a warhead comprising 3,417lb (1,550kg) of high explosive.

effectively beaten but refused to concede the fact before the dropping of the atomic bombs on Hiroshima and Nagasaki in August 1945: in 1939, before the outbreak of the Pacific war, Japan had possessed 2,337 merchant ships, but by August 1945 this total had been reduced to 231. Some of the 4,000,000 tons of shipping succumbed to air attack, but the majority of losses were the victims primarily of American, and to a lesser extent British and Dutch, submarine attack directly with torpedoes or indirectly with mines. The Americans lost 60 submarines during the war, although the Japanese had claimed 486 – the true figure may be accounted a relatively small price to have paid for so magnificent a victory.

The American submarines did not limit their attacks to the vital Japanese merchant marine, but supplied scouting and aircrew recovery lines for the major offensive operations of the Pacific fleet, and also played a major part in sinking Japanese warships, including eight aircraft carriers and 12

By comparison with their counterparts in the western theatre, both German and British, and with their Japanese opponents in the eastern theatre, the crews of American submarines enjoyed a fairly high level of habitability despite the general accolade of 'pig boats' for their submarines. This habitability factor combined with good food to maintain the morale and fighting efficiency of American submarines at a high pitch throughout their patrols.

Left: Built by the Portsmouth Navy Yard and launched in May 1941, the Drum was a typical member of the 'Gato' class and survived World War II. The boat was finally stricken in June 1968 and hulked as a naval monument at Mobile, Alabama. The basic details of the 'Gato' class included surfaced and submerged displacements of 1,526 and 2,424 tons respectively, a length of 311ft 9in (95.02m), a two-shaft propulsion arrangement with 5,400hp (4,026kW) diesel engines and 2,740hp (2,043kW) electric motors for surfaced and submerged speeds of 20.25 and 8.75 knots respectively, a crew of 85, and an armament of ten 21in (533mm) tubes for 24 torpedoes plus one 3in (76mm) deck gun that was later replaced by a 5in (127mm) weapon and supplemented by one 40mm and two 20mm anti-aircraft guns.

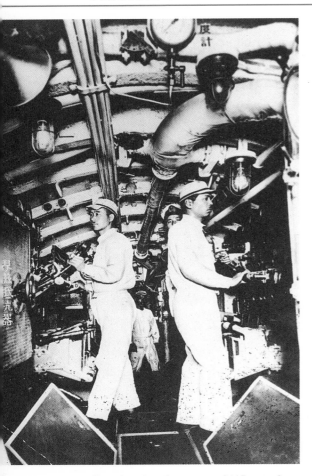

Completed to the extent of 115 out of a planned 406 boats, the 'Type D Koryu' class of midget submarines had a submerged displacement of 59.33 tons, a submerged speed of 16 knots, a crew of five, and an armament of two 18in (457mm) tubes for two torpedoes.

cruisers. The most telling of the former was the sinking of the huge *Shinano* by the *Archerfish* in November 1944, and a classic example of the latter was the destruction of the heavy cruisers *Atago* and *Maya* in October 1944 in an ambush by the *Dace* and *Darter*, which also severely damaged a third cruiser in the same action.

The Americans introduced the 'wolf pack' concept to their Pacific submarine operations during 1943, but by this time were so rampant that three-boat groups were deemed adequate to overwhelm even convoys supported by the indifferent escort vessels that the Japanese had started to build too late and in wholly inadequate numbers.

The complete superiority of the American submarine arm in the Pacific should not be allowed to disguise the fact that the Japanese submariners also had their moments of triumph, most notably in August 1942 when the *I-26* torpedoed and severely damaged the aircraft carrier *Saratoga*, and in September 1942 when the *I-15* torpedoed and severely damaged the battleship *North Carolina* and the *I-19* sank the aircraft carrier *Wasp*. These were relatively isolated instances, however, for in general the size of the Japanese submarines and the relative lack of tactical guile displayed by their commanders played into the hands of the American escort forces, of which one of the stars was the escort destroyer *England* that sank six Japanese submarines in the course of 12 days during May 1944.

Throughout the war, Japanese submariners urged on their high command the paramount importance of attacking targets other than the Pacific fleet's primary warships, but these pleas fell on deaf ears until a time late in 1942, when the import of the first American amphibious assaults on island groups in the Central Pacific finally sank into the minds of the Japanese naval high command. Even then, the response of these senior officers was ill-considered: realising the importance of these American assaults, they ordered virtually suicidal submarine attacks on the very well-protected ships of the landing forces, and also the use of submarines to transport men and equipment into bases that might become the next targets for American attack.

This use of attack submarines for the transport role was hardly a cost-effective method, as the British had realised during their supply runs to

The officer of the deck scans the horizon for ships and, perhaps more crucially, attacking warplanes, from his position on the conning tower of the *Batfish* during May 1945. A submarine of the 'Gato' class, the *Batfish* was built by the Portsmouth Navy Yard and launched in May 1943. The boat survived World War II, and was stricken in November 1969 before being hulked as a naval monument.

The boats of the 'Gato' (illustrated) and closely related 'Balao' classes bore the brunt of the US Navy's submarine warfare effort in the Pacific during World War II, and proved highly successful in the interdiction of the Japanese seaborne lines of communication, both naval and mercantile.

Malta in 1942, which were most effectively undertaken by a converted minelayer supported by a number of other boats. The Japanese response was therefore the construction of specialised transport submarines. The first of these were the 12 out of a projected 104 units of the 'Type D1' class. These boats had surfaced and submerged displacements of 1,779 and 2,215 tons respectively, a considerable range, armament limited to one 5.5in (140mm) deck gun and two 25mm cannon, and provision for a payload that could comprise 82 tons of freight or 110 men landed with the aid of two 14ft 6in (4.4m) boats.

Given the intense rivalry between itself and the Japanese navy, which it felt never gave adequate consideration to army demands, the Japanese army paralleled the navy move into transport submarines and commissioned its own type as the 'Yu 1' class, of which 12 were built. These were smaller boats, with a submerged displacement of 370 tons, and could carry 40 tons of freight.

Japan built a number of other submarine classes later in World War II, but the only two worthy of mention here are the huge 'Type STo' and midget 'Kaiten' types. Ordered in 1942 as the largest submarines envisaged up to that time, the 'Type STo' class was proposed at more than 18 units of which only three were completed with a crew of 144 men, a submerged displacement of 6,560 tons, the phenomenal surfaced range of 37,500 miles (60,350km) at 14 knots, and an armament that included eight 21in (533mm) tubes for 20 torpedoes, one 5.5in (140mm) deck gun, ten 25mm anti-aircraft cannon in two triple and four single mountings, and, most impressively of all, three special attack seaplanes (for which four torpedoes and 15 bombs were carried) that were designed specifically for attacks on the lock gates in

Opposite top: The 'Type STo' class submarine *I-400* comes alongside the US Navy's submarine tender Proteus to surrender in August 1945. After a thorough examination and evaluation, the submarine was scuttled off the US coast in 1946.

Opposite bottom: The fact that Germany was still planning to prosecute the submarine war at the time of her defeat is highlighted by this scene in Hamburg during May 1945, when large numbers of incomplete 'Type XXI' class submarines were discovered.

Below: A standard unit of the 'Tench' class, the *Torsk* was built by the Portsmouth Navy Yard and launched in September 1944.

the Panama Canal, whose destruction would have required American ships to round Cape Horn as a means of transiting between the Pacific and Atlantic Oceans.

The 'Kaiten' classes, of which four types were built, were designed for the *kamikaze* role, and were therefore suicide craft based on the design of the Japanese torpedo. The only operational model was the 'Kaiten 4' class, of which 419 were completed with a conventional torpedo motor rather than the hydrogen peroxide motors of the experimental 'Kaiten 2' and 'Kaiten 3' classes. Considerable effort was expended on these essentially defensive craft, which achieved no successes.

During the course of World War II, the Japanese submarine arm lost 149 of its 245 major boats excluding midget types and the German and Italian boats that were taken over in very small numbers.

By a quirk typical of history, it was the Americans' feeling that Japan's submarine arm had failed to live up to its real potential and was therefore a negligible risk, that was responsible for the last US catastrophe of World War II and its worst naval disaster of all time. The heavy cruiser *Indianapolis*, having delivered the first atomic bomb to the Mariana Islands, was steaming for Leyte in the Philippines. Believing that there was no real threat from the Japanese, the ship was neither escorted nor zigzagging and passed straight through the patrol line of the *I-58*, which fired a full spread of six torpedoes. Two of these hit, and the *Indianapolis* sank in a mere 12 minutes. It was three days later before anyone in the Philippines realised that the cruiser was overdue, and the belated rescue attempt meant that many of the men who had survived the sinking had meanwhile succumbed to wounds, the weather condition and sharks. The total loss of American life in this last Japanese submarine victory of the war was 883.

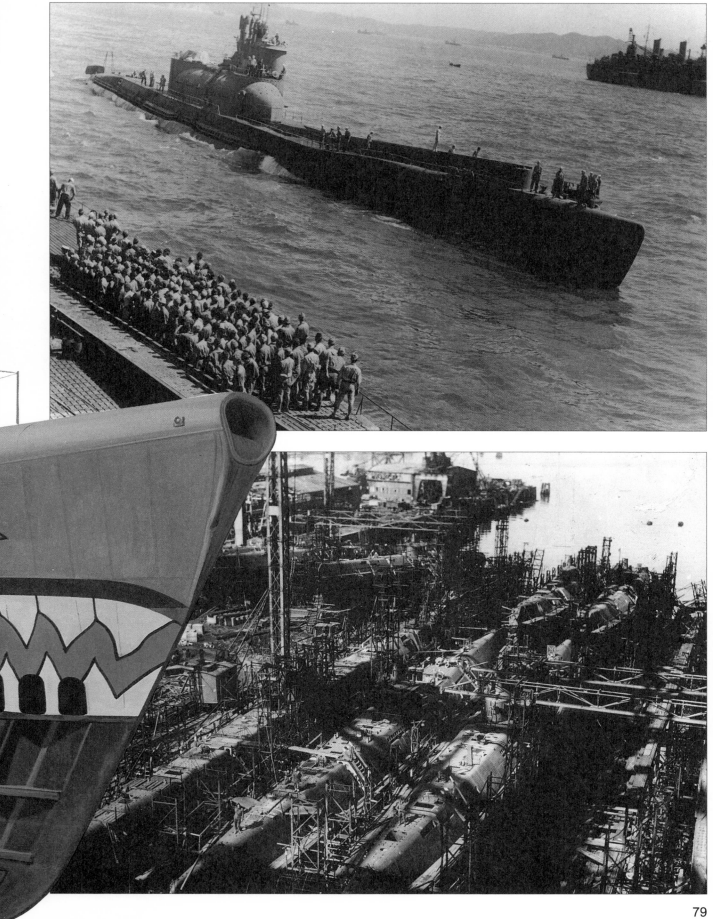

The Post-War Submarine

EVEN as the final defeat of Japan was being encompassed, teams of technical officers from the victorious Allied powers were scouring German ports, research centres and manufacturing facilities for information about the German submarines that had so nearly proved decisive. The boats in which the Allies were most interested were the conventionally powered 'Type XXI' class and the Walther-powered 'Type XVII' and 'Type XXIII' classes. With the immediate pressure of war lifted, the Allied powers concentrated their attention initially on the 'Type XXI' class design that was currently the most advanced conventionally powered submarine in the world. The main concepts learned from examination of these boats was the desirability of a highly streamlined hull with the minimum number of protuberances (including the deck gun), the streamlining of the conning tower with its platforms and periscope standards into a long sail, and the adoption of the *Schnorchel* as a standard feature that became known to the Americans as a snorkel and to the British as a snort.

The adoption of these features allowed the creation of new classes of submarine notable for underwater performance that was faster, quieter and longer-ranged, and the introduction of these new classes bought time for the primary submarine-building nations (the UK, USA and USSR) to consider their next moves. These included a practical investigation of the Walther system, although the USA soon dropped out of the running because of the dangers of the system, and by the mid-1950s all three nations had decided that the adoption of the Walther system was not a satisfactory solution to the question of how to produce true surface-independent submarines to replace the surface-reliant submersibles, which is what virtually all underwater vessels had been up to this time.

The solution, as the Americans had already realised, was the adoption of a nuclear propulsion arrangement in place of the diesel and electric or diesel-electric systems used in most recent submarines. This involved the creation of a shielded nuclear reactor whose controllable heat output could be used for the generation within a closed-cycle system of the steam that would power turbines for propulsion and/or the generation of electricity before being condensed back into water for return to the heat exchanger attached to the reactor. This would obviate the need for large batteries, although a number would be retained for emergency use, and though the system presented no major technical difficulties at the conceptual level, its development to a practical level demanded the injection of considerable capital and resources before a safe and usefully compact system could be prepared for submarine use.

While this longer-term solution to submarine propulsion and power was being planned and prepared, submarine designers continued to develop

A member of the 'Benjamin Franklin' class, the *George Bancroft* was originally armed with Poseidon submarine-launched ballistic missiles but was later modified to carry the considerably more capable Trident I missile. The boat was built by Electric Boat between August 1963 and December 1964, and was commissioned in January 1966.

conventionally powered boats. The US Navy's immediate response to the implications of the German submarines of World War II was the 'GUPPY' (Greater Underwater Propulsive Power) programme in which many surviving units of the 'Gato', 'Balao' and 'Tench' classes, together with the uncompleted units of the last class, were revised or completed with a lengthened and more streamlined hull/sail combination, larger batteries and a snorkel. Others of these boats were revised for experimental purposes, including the evaluation of the submarine for underway replenishment of oil and supplies at sea, and as the launch platform for guided missiles.

This last plan was of greater long-term importance, and started with the conversion in 1948-49 of the *Carbonero* and *Cusk* to carry and launch the 'Loon' surface-to-surface missile, which was an American development of the Fieseler Fi 103 weapon better known in the West as the V-1 of World War II. The trials confirmed the feasibility of the system, and the US Navy then authorised the development of the Regulus I, which was a substantial turbojet-powered missile intended for the anti-ship role, and the *Barbero* and

A member of the definitive 'Tench 'class of fleet submarines completed late in World War II the USS *Amberjack* was launched in July 1944. and the boats features included an armament of ten 21in(533nn) tubes (six forward and four stern) for 24 torpedoes, one 5in (127mm) deck gun, one 40mm anti-aircraft gun and one 20mm anti-aircraft cannon.

The GUPPY Programme

IN 1945 the US Navy found itself with a large force of related 'Gato', 'Balao' and 'Tench' class fleet submarines that had proved very successful against the Japanese in the Pacific war but had now been rendered technically obsolete by the advent of the German 'Type XXI' class submarine. For the longer term the US Navy was planning the introduction of nuclear-powered submarines, but now required a short-term expedient to maintain a credible submarine force at a time of worsening relations with the USSR, which was known to be developing a major submarine capability based on the 'Type XXI' design. The US Navy's solution was therefore the GUPPY (Greater Underwater Propulsive Power) programme in which four reload torpedoes, part of the fresh water tankage and deck gun magazine volume were used for increased battery capacity for greater submerged speed and endurance in concert with an exterior that was streamlined by the deletion of all guns, the remodelling of the casing, and the fairing of the conning tower into a low-drag 'sail'. The two 'GUPPY I' class prototype conversions had no snorkel, but this was added in the following 12 'GUPPY II' class conversions that introduced a higher-power but very expensive type of battery. The next 12 'GUPPY IA' conversions (two of them for the Dutch navy) therefore reverted to the original type of battery even though this meant a sacrifice of 1 knot of submerged speed; at the same time 16 boats were converted to the more austere Fleet Snorkel standard with a GUPPY-type sail and snorkel but without the remodelled hull. Finally there came 16 'GUPPY IIA' class conversions with one main engine removed to allow the relocation of some secondary machinery as a means of optimising sonar performance. The 'GUPPY' classes were now taken in hand under the FRAM (Fleet Rehabilitation And Modernization) programme, nine 'GUPPY II' class boats being revised to 'GUPPY III' class standard with the hull lengthened by 10ft (3.05m) to allow the incorporation of a plotting room and a longer sail as well as a new fire-control system that would allow use of the Mk 45 Astor nuclear anti-submarine torpedo. Further development of the concept introduced a sail of plastic construction, and a number of existing fleet boats were upgraded to an improved Fleet Snorkel standard with the plastic sail. Once the US Navy had started to introduce nuclear-powered attack submarines, many of the 'GUPPY' boats were transferred to friendly navies, some of which still operate the submarines in limited numbers.

The *Skate* was the lead boat of the four-strong 'Skate' class of attack submarines, which were the first 'production line' submarines of the nuclear-powered type. The boats were commissioned between December 1957 and December 1959 after construction by four yards (one commercial and three navy) to provide experience in the building of such submarines. The basic details of the class included surfaced and submerged displacements of 2,550 and 2,848 tons respectively, a length of 267ft 8in (81.6m), a two-shaft propulsion arrangement with a single nuclear reactor supplying steam to 6,600hp (4,921kW) geared steam turbines for a submerged speed of about 20 knots, a crew of 84.

Intended for the coastal role, the *U-29* of the 18-strong West German 'Type 206' class was built by Howaldtswerke at Kiel and launched in November 1973. The basic details of the class, which is typical of the high-performance conventionally powered submarines of the period, include surfaced and submerged displacements of 456 and 500 tons respectively, a length of 159ft 6in (48.6m), a single-shaft propulsion arrangement of the diesel-electric type with a 1,500hp (1,118 kW) electric motor and 1,200hp (895kW) diesel engines for surfaced and submerged speeds of 10 and 17.5 knots respectively, a crew of 21, and an armament of eight 21in (533m) tubes for 16 wire-guided torpedoes or mines, supplemented as required by a further 24 mines in external containers.

Tunny were later adapted to carry two of these missiles in cylindrical hangars. Further development of the Regulus concept resulted in the considerably larger Regulus II with strategic capability, and as this more massive weapon could only be carried by larger submarines, the US Navy ordered the *Grayback* and *Growler*, which were built in the period between 1952 and 1958 with two large cylindrical hangars built into the forward casing. The Regulus II system was abandoned after only five years, but the submarines associated with it were retained in service after conversion as transports for amphibious warfare and special forces teams.

The USA's last series-built submarines of the conventionally powered type were the 'Tang' class of attack submarines of which six were completed in the period between 1949 and 1952, and finally the 'Barbel' class of attack submarines of which just three were built between 1956 and 1959. The design of the 'Darter' class was based on that of the 'Type XXI' submarine, and the design may therefore be compared with the Soviet 'Whiskey' class, which was built in very large numbers although it was in no way as

A conventionally powered patrol submarine, the *Ghazi* is one of the Pakistani navy's four French 'Daphné' class boats bought as one ex-Portuguese and three new-build vessels. The type has surfaced and submerged displacements of 869 and 1,043 tons respectively, a length of 190ft 0in (57.8m), a two-shaft propulsion arrangement with 1,300hp (969kW) diesel engines and a 1,600hp (1,193kW) electric motor for surfaced and surfaced speeds of 13.5 and 16 knots respectively, a crew of 45, and an armament of 12 21.7in (550mm) torpedo tubes located as eight in the bows and four in the stern.

sophisticated a type as the American design. Although obsolescent by American standards at the time of its appearance, the 'Barbel' class design nonetheless remains interesting as that in which a number of hitherto experimental features were combined for the first time in an operational series. These features included the type of low-drag 'teardrop' hull first tested in the US Navy's experimental *Albacore* launched in 1953, a single large propeller turning comparatively slowly for a reduced noise 'signature', all the control systems centralised in an 'attack centre' for fully optimised operational capability and, as a retrofit, the diving planes on the bows replaced by planes on the sides of the sail.

This period after the end of World War II was characterised by a rapid decline in relations between the USA and the USSR, now indisputably the world's two superpowers, and the equally rapid development of a 'cold war' between these superpowers and their allies. The USSR had quickly followed the USA's lead into nuclear weapons capability, and the USA feared a major air assault with such weapons. Early warning was therefore of paramount importance for defence, and the USA made extensive use of ships and submarines fitted with long-range surveillance radar for timely warning of any imminent Soviet attack on the continental USA. One of the most fascinating of these boats, most of which were converted from conventionally powered attack submarines, was the *Triton*, which was built in 1959 as one of the first nuclear-powered boats and was for its time the largest submarine in the world, with a submerged displacement of 7,773

Built by Electric Boat between November 1962 and June 1968 for a commissioning date in August 1969, the US Navy's conventionally powered *Dolphin* was designed and built as a research submarine with a perfectly cylindrical hull 18ft 0in (5.49m) in diameter closed off at each end with a hemispherical bulkhead. Extensive use was made of alloys and plastics, and the boat was used mainly for deep-diving and acoustic work as well as oceanographic research.

tons and a two-shaft nuclear propulsion arrangement for surfaced and submerged speeds of 27 and 20 knots respectively, the former allowing rapid transit between operational areas.

Throughout this period, little was known about the development of Soviet submarines. It gradually became clear, however, that Soviet developments from the mid-1940s had resulted in delivery in the early 1950s of the 'Whiskey' class conventionally powered submarine in large numbers for the attack role, to which were later added the radar picket and, from 1961, missile launch roles in four and 12 boats respectively. Production of this class eventually amounted to 236 boats, and from 1961 a considerable number of these useful submarines were transferred to the navies of friendly nations.

The next major type to appear was the 'Zulu' class, whose operational capability with a conventional propulsion arrangement was confirmed in 1952, after early attempts to create an effective version of the Walther propulsion system had failed. Some 26 of the type were built as longer-ranged equivalents of the medium-range 'Whiskey' class, and of these boats six were completed or converted as strategic missile submarines, with the rear part of their sails adapted for the vertical launch of two ballistic missiles. Built at about the same time to a total of 22 units, the 'Golf' class was basically an enlarged version of the 'Zulu' class design with a longer sail carrying three vertically launched missiles.

The development of Soviet conventionally powered submarines continued with the 'Romeo' class of which 17 were built between 1958 and

Lead submarine of the five-strong 'George Washington' class and commissioned in December 1959, the *George Washington* was the US Navy's first nuclear-powered ballistic missile submarine and as such opened a new era in strategic warfare. The class was typified by surfaced and submerged displacements of 5,959 and 6,709 tons respectively, a length of 381ft 8in (116.4m), a single-shaft propulsion arrangement with one reactor supplying steam to 15,000hp (1,118kW) geared steam turbines for a submerged speed of about 20 knots, a crew of 112, and an armament of 16 vertically launched Polaris missiles and six 21in (533mm) torpedo tubes.

Whereas the 'George Washington' class had been produced by adapting 'Skipjack' class attack submarines already under construction with a lengthened hull to accommodate the missile section, the following 'Ethan Allen' class of nuclear-powered missile submarines was designed specifically for its task although it drew considerably from the 'Thresher' class attack submarine in features such as its stronger hull material and improved silencing features. The boats also introduced passive towed-array sonar for improved defensive capability. The basic details of the 'Ethan Allen' class, here exemplified by the *Ethan Allen* that was built by Electric Boat between September 1959 and November 1960 for commissioning in August 1961, included surfaced and submerged displacements of 6,946 and 7,884 tons respectively, a length of 410ft 5in (125.1m), a single-shaft propulsion arrangement with one reactor supplying steam to 15,000hp (11,18kW) geared steam turbines for a submerged speed of about 20 knots, a crew of 110, and an armament of 16 vertically launched Polaris missiles and four 21in (533mm) torpedo tubes.

Right: Built by Nackums and the Karlskrona Navy Dockyard between 1976 and 1981, the three conventionally powered attack submarines of the Swedish navy's 'Näcken' class of attack submarines have a teardrop-shaped hull.

1961 as successors to the 'Whiskey' class with two more torpedo tubes together with greater range and diving depth, the 'Quebec' class of which 30 were built between 1954 and 1957 to replace the pre-war 'M' class boats in the coastal role and fitted with a closed-cycle propulsion arrangement, and the 'Foxtrot' class of which 76 were built between 1958 and 1967 as successors to the 'Zulu' class with reduced surface range but significantly improved underwater speed.

The USSR followed the USA's lead into the development of nuclear-powered submarines, but unlike its ideological foe did not entirely abandon the conventionally powered submarine. Between the early 1970s and 1982, therefore, the Soviet navy received 18 'Kilo' class submarines to replace the units of the 'Foxtrot' class with an improved type whose larger internal

The *Thresher* was lead boat of the US Navy's second full class of nuclear-powered attack submarines, which was built to the extent of 14 boats with a modified teardrop-shaped hull with the torpedo tubes relocated to the amidships position thereby leaving the bow entirely clear for the advanced sonar that was the core of the class's anti-submarine capability. The *Thresher* was lost in the Atlantic in April 1963, and the class was later renamed as the 'Permit' class after its second boat. The details of the class included surfaced and submerged displacements of 3,705 and 4,311 tons respectively, a length of 278ft 6in (84.9m) increased in some of the later boats, a single-shaft propulsion arrangement with one reactor supplying steam to 15,000hp (1,118kW) geared steam turbines for a submerged speed of 30 knots, a crew of 94, and an armament of four 21in (533mm) tubes for 22 torpedoes.

volume is used for improved habitability, greater battery capacity, and a larger weapon load. The final development of Soviet conventional submarine thinking was the 'Kilo' class, which entered production in 1978 or 1979 with a considerably better hull form than the 'Tango' class for improved underwater speed.

Although the USA and the USSR have largely dominated the technological and constructional aspects of submarine development in the period since World War II, a number of other countries have contributed and in the process have created or maintained significant submarine warfare capabilities.

At the end of World War II, the UK's most important submarines were those of the 'S' and 'T' classes, complemented during the late 1940s by a number of 'A' class boats designed in World War II for long-range operations in the Pacific but completed too late for this campaign. The 'S' and earlier 'T' class boats were of riveted rather than welded construction, and were therefore deemed unsuitable for major development after the war even though five 'T' class boats were given a more streamlined casing, but eight of the later 'T' class boats and 14 of the 18 'A' class boats were taken in hand

Opposite: The Italian navy's *Romeo Romei* was built as the US Navy's *Harder* of the six-strong 'Tang' class, which was the American attempt to exploit the concept of the German 'Type XXI' class submarine and thereby match the capabilities of the Soviet 'Whiskey' class that was in the event built in much larger numbers. The basic details of the design included surfaced and submerged displacements of 1,560 and 2,260 tons respectively, a length of 287ft 0in (87.5m), a two-shaft propulsion arrangement with 4,500hp (3,355kW) diesel engines and 5,600hp (4,175kW) electric motors for a surfaced and submerged speed of 16 knots, a crew of 83, and an armament of eight 21in (533mm) torpedo tubes located as six in the bows and two in the stern.

Built to the extent of 23 boats, the 'Golf' class was the USSR's first attempt to create a submarine with vertically launched ballistic missile capability, in this instance with only three tubes for SS-N-4 missiles that could be launched only after the submarine had surfaced, and a conventional propulsion arrangement with three shafts driven by 6,000hp (4,474kW) diesel engines and 5,300hp (3,952kW) electric motors for a submerged speed of 12 knots.

during the 1950s for modernisation along the lines of the American 'GUPPY' programme, with a lengthened and more streamlined hull containing an uprated propulsion arrangement and more battery cells for a doubled submerged speed. This provided the Royal Navy with a useful attack submarine capability into the late 1950s, but further development was centred on new construction in the form of the eight boats of the 'Porpoise' class built between 1956 and 1961, making use of the lessons learned from captured German data and British post-war developments in the creation of a type notable for its generally good performance and exceptional quietness. Further development of the concepts embodied in the 'Porpoise' class, individually small but collectively large, resulted in the 'Oberon' class, of

The *Seawolf*, built between September 1953 and July 1955 by Electric Boat for commissioning in March 1957, was in essence a prototype attack submarine with a nuclear powerplant based on a sodium- rather than pressurised water-cooled reactor. There were considerable problems with this powerplant, however, and the US Navy therefore decided to concentrate of pressurised water-cooled reactors.

which 13 were built for the Royal Navy between 1957 and 1967, with another 14 delivered to export customers. To complete the story of British conventional submarine design, mention must be made of the superb 'Upholder' class ordered in the early 1980s to replace the 'Oberon' class. Notably quiet and equipped with anti-ship missiles as well as advanced torpedoes all controlled for a high-quality fire-control system, production and operational service have been truncated as a result of the 'peace dividend' accruing from the collapse of the USSR in the late 1980s and the effective end of the 'cold war'.

In 1945, France was faced with the immense task of rebuilding not only the country's armed forces but also the industrial base required to equip these forces with weapons of indigenous design and manufacture. So far as its navy's submarine arm was concerned, a start was made with the receipt of four British 'S' class boats for training purposes and the completion to a modernised standard of five 'La Creole' class submarines from incomplete 'L'Aurore' class hulls that had survived the war. This bought time for French

The *Nautilus* was the world's first nuclear-powered submarine, and with its pressurised water-cooled reactor proved considerably more successful than the slightly later Seawolf with its sodium-cooled reactor.

designers to assimilate the latest thinking in submarine concepts, and the result comprised the six boats of the 'Narval' class of ocean-going submarine, all completed in the period between 1957 and 1960, and the four boats of the 'Aréthuse' class of sea-going submarine, completed between 1957 and 1958 after design as the world's first dedicated hunter-killer submarines. Between 1964 and 1970, the 'Aréthuse' class was supplemented and finally supplanted by the slightly larger 'Daphné' class, of which 11 were completed as smaller counterparts to the ocean-going 'Narval' class boats. Several more 'Daphné' class boats were built in France for Pakistan (three boats), Portugal (four boats) and South Africa (three boats), and an additional four were produced under licence in Spain as 'S 61' class units.

The three other northern European countries that have designed and built their own submarines are the Netherlands, Sweden, and Germany. Dutch design and production have been responsible for the four-strong 'Dolfijn' class with a unique triple hull design, the 'Zwaardvis' class of two attack submarines, and the 'Walrus' class of four improved attack submarines. Swedish design and construction have yielded the six boats of the 'Hajen' class based on the 'Type XXI' design, the six boats of the 'Draken' class, the five boats of the 'Sjöormen' class of teardrop-hulled attack submarine with an X-shaped arrangement of surfaces at the stern, the three boats of the smaller 'Näcken' class of attack submarines, and the four advanced boats of the 'Västergötland' class of attack submarines.

Once allowed to re-arm in the mid-1950s as part of the North Atlantic Treaty Organization (NATO), which was faced with the threat of Soviet-led aggression by the forces of the Warsaw Pact countries, West Germany started to rebuild its armed forces with emphasis on the ground and air elements that would have to play a key part in the defence of West Germany, the most likely avenue for a communist

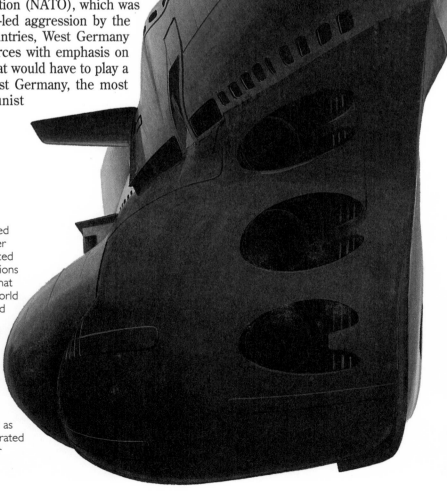

The British moved into nuclear-powered submarine construction somewhat later than the Americans, and therefore placed greater initial reliance on updated versions of the conventionally powered types that had done well in the later stages of World War II. One of the classes that received a modernisation was the 'T' class of ocean-going submarines, of which five were moderately improved with a streamlined casing and sail as the 'T Streamline' class and eight were more significantly upgraded with the same improve-ments as well as a lengthened hull, two more electric motors and increased battery capacity as the 'T Conversion' class. The boat illustrated is the *Thrasher*, which was not used for either of the programmes and was therefore scrapped in 1947.

offensive. The navy was not neglected, however, and plans were laid for the creation of small but high-quality elements responsible for operations in the western end of the Baltic Sea and in the southern part of the North Sea. Part of this capability was inevitably vested in a new submarine arm, and to provide an initial training capability the new West German navy raised two 'Type XXIII' and one 'Type XXI' submarines for reconstruction with the type of electric propulsion (the diesels being used only as generators) that has been used for all subsequent German submarine classes: the boats became the two 'Hai' and one 'Wilhelm Bauer' class submarines.

The new navy's first operational submarines were the three (originally 12) units of the 'Type 201' coastal boat with a submerged displacement of only 433 tons, the high submerged speed of 17.5 knots and the heavy armament of eight 21in (533mm) tubes for eight torpedoes, but only limited range and indifferent habitability for the crew of 21. Further development of the same basic concept led to the 11 units of the slightly larger 'Type 205' class, which was not notably successful, and then the successful 'Type 206' class of which 18 units were completed with features to reduce underwater noise and a capability that allows the use of advanced torpedoes which

The Soviet submarine type known in the West as the 'Whiskey Twin Cylinder' class was a conversion of the standard 'Whiskey' class conventionally powered attack submarine with a side-by-side pair of cylindrical container-launchers abaft the sail for two SS-N-3 'Shaddock' nuclear-tipped cruise missiles.

Le Redoutable is the lead submarine of France's five-strong first class of nuclear-powered ballistic missile submarines built by the Arsenal de Cherbourg between 1964 and 1982.

receive their guidance commands via a wire system from the submarine's fire-control computer. Germany's latest submarine class is the highly advanced 'Type 212' with hybrid fuel cell/battery propulsion for considerably extended underwater endurance.

The design of these boats was the responsibility of IKL (Ingenieurkontor Lübeck), which has become a world leader in the design of conventionally powered submarines that have secured considerable success in the export and licence-built markets. Among IKL's designs are the 'Type 207' class used by Denmark and Norway and the 'Type 209' used in a number of differently sized subvariants by Argentina, Brazil, Chile, Colombia, Ecuador, Greece, India, Indonesia, Israel, Peru, South Korea, Taiwan, Turkey and Venezuela.

The only other European country to have designed and built advanced conventionally powered submarines is Italy, whose post-war career in this field began with the four 'Toti' class attack submarines optimised for the coastal role and then progressed, via the four larger 'Sauro' class and four 'Sauro (Improved)' class attack submarines optimised for the sea-going role, to the 'S 90' class modern type with excellent capabilities.

Laid down in the early 1950s and all commissioned by 1960, the six boats of the 'Narval' class, here exemplified by the *Narval*, were the first French submarines designed to incorporate the concepts first revealed in the German 'Type XXI' class of World War II.

The helmsman's position in *Le Redoutable* reveals how modern submarines are controlled in a manner similar to that used for aircraft although there is, of course, no exterior view!

This view of the US Navy's *Nautilus* under way reveals that the core design was derived from that of the 'Type XXI' adapted for a nuclear powerplant. The teardrop-shaped hull characteristic of most modern submarines was adopted only later.

The only other country in the world to have designed and built advanced conventionally powered submarines is Japan, whose first post-war boat was the *Oyashio*, completed in 1960 with a submerged displacement of 1,420 tons, a submerged speed of 19 knots, and an armament of four 21in (533mm) torpedo tubes in the bows, and a wholly conservative design based on a whale-shaped hull. There followed the four submarines of the two-boat 'Hayashio' and 'Natsushio' classes with a shorter and fuller hull for good safety features and excellent habitability, but with submerged displacements of only 800 and 850 tons respectively, they were limited in capability to coastal work. The size was nearly doubled in the five submarines of the 'Oshio' class that followed between 1965 and 1969 as Japan's first post-war

The 'Type 209' class submarine designed in Germany has become the most common type of conventionally powered submarine in the world, helped considerably by its high performance and availability in several forms allowing any navy to choose a model ideally suited to its requirements. This is the *Islay* of the Peruvian navy, which operates six of the boats, and is an example of the 'Type 209/1' or 'Type 1200' class with surfaced and submerged displacements of 1,185 and 1,285 tons respectively, a length of 183ft 5in (55.9m), a single-shaft propulsion arrangement of the diesel-electric type with 9,440hp (7,040kW) diesel engines and 4,960hp (3,700kW) electric motor for surfaced and submerged speeds of 10 and 22 knots respectively, a crew of 31, and an armament of eight 21in (533mm) tubes in the bows for 14 wire-guided torpedoes or 28 mines.

The *Huancavilca* is one of two 'Type 209/2' or 'Type 1300' class submarines operated by the Ecuadorian navy with details that include surfaced and submerged displacements of 1,285 and 1,390 tons respectively, a length of 195ft 2in (59.5m), a single-shaft propulsion arrangement of the diesel-electric type with 9,440hp (7,040kW) diesel engines and 4,960hp (3,700kW) electric motor for surfaced and submerged speeds of 11 and 21.5 knots respectively, a crew of 33, and an armament of eight 21in (533mm) tubes in the bows for 16 torpedoes or 32 mines.

attack submarines of the ocean-going type, but Japanese submarine concepts finally began to reach maturity in 1971 with the delivery of the first of seven 'Uzushio' class boats with a teardrop-shaped hull, a displacement of 3,600 tons, a submerged speed of 20 knots, and an armament of six 21in torpedo tubes located amidships to leave the optimum bow location for the sonar. From 1980 there followed the 10 boats of the 'Yuushio' class developed from the 'Uzushio' class with deeper diving capability and improved electronics, and the most modern of the Japanese submarine classes, entering service from 1990, is the six-strong 'Harushio' class with a

The *Enrico Toti*, completed in January 1968, was the name boat of the Italian navy's four 'Toti' class conventionally powered submarines with surfaced and submerged displacements of 460 and 585 tons respectively, a length of 151ft 6in (46.2m), a single-shaft propulsion arrangement of the diesel-electric type with two diesel engines and 2,200hp (1,640kW) electric motor.

Many submarines surplus to the requirements of the UK and USA in the period after the end of World War II were passed or sold to the navies of friendly nations seeking to develop their navies. Typical of this tendency was this boat, the ex-British *Truncheon* of the 'T' class, which was sold to the Israeli navy in the mid-1960s as the *Dolphin* together with two similar boats.

submerged displacement of 2,750 tons, a submerged speed of more than 20 knots, and an armament of six 21in tubes for wire-guided torpedoes as well as underwater-launched Harpoon anti-ship missiles.

As these conventionally powered developments were under way, the USA was pressing ahead with the development of the nuclear-powered submarine initially for the attack role and then, in a considerably larger form, for the ballistic missile launch role. The starting point for the concept of the dedicated attack (hunter-killer) submarine combined high underwater performance (especially in speed and endurance/range) offered by the nuclear propulsion arrangement, after effective quietening features had been developed, and the much-enhanced ability to detect

---

The Sinking of the *Belgrano*

It is believed that the only time a nuclear-powered attack submarine has been used to sink an enemy warship was in May 1982, when as part of the naval operations concerned with the British recapture of the Falkland Islands from an Argentine invasion force, the attack submarine Conqueror of the 'Churchill' class torpedoed and sank the Argentine heavy cruiser General Belgrano, an ex-American ship of the 'Brooklyn' class with a displacement of 13,645 tons and an armament of fifteen 6in (152mm) guns in five triple turrets. Although the Argentine ship, escorted by two ex-American destroyers, was slightly outside the total exclusion zone declared by the British, she remained a distinct threat to the British naval forces preparing for the landings on the Falklands, and the decision was taken at the highest level to sink her. The Conqueror had been shadowing the General Belgrano with passive sonar, and on receipt of the 'sink' order from London, the captain of the Conqueror ordered the start of the attack plot on the DCB wire-control system and decided to use the elderly Mk 8** torpedo, designed in the period before World War II, rather than the more modern Mk 24 Tigerfish wire-guided torpedo, as the older weapon's 750lb (340kg) warhead was better suited to the destruction of a large surface vessel than the 331lb (150kg) warhead of the Mk 24, and as the Mk 8** could be fired in a salvo of four while the Mk 24 could be fired only in a salvo of two. The four torpedoes were fired from a range of about 1,400yds (1,280m) with their gyros set to generate a curved course and so confuse the Argentines about the position of the attacker. As soon as the torpedoes had been fired, the Conqueror dived to 985ft (300m) and soon heard two large explosions: the first torpedo detonated on the port side of the hull under the after 5in (127mm) secondary gun director and the second just forward of 'A' turret. The ship sank in about 45 minutes, taking with her the bodies of 321 Argentine sailors, the vast majority of them killed in the initial explosions. Some 880 other men were later rescued from the water by other Argentine ships.

Opposite: To provide industry and the navy with experience in the design and operation of a submarine capable of carrying vertically launched ballistic missiles, the French navy commissioned the Gymnote as an experimental conventionally powered boat with four of the M-1 missiles planned for the country's first nuclear-powered missile submarines, together with the associated fire-control and inertial navigation systems. The boat was launched in March 1964 and commissioned in October 1966.

Thought to be the fastest boats currently in service, the attack submarines of the Soviet (now Russian) 'Alfa' class can reach a submerged speed of 45 knots with a single-shaft propulsion arrangement based on two liquid metal-cooled reactors supplying steam to two sets of turbo-alternators generating the current for a 46,940hp (35,000kW) electric motor. The 'Alfa' class is also based on a hull of high-strength titanium for a maximum diving depth of 3,280ft (1,000m) although the normal operating limit is 1,970ft (600m).

and track enemy submarines provided by modern sonar (sound navigation and ranging).

These features became feasible in the early 1950s, and resulted in two pioneering boats, namely the *Nautilus* and the *Seawolf* as the world's first nuclear-powered submarines, in each case with an armament of six 21in (533m) tubes in the bows for the targets whose presence, bearing and range were indicated by the advanced BQS-4 sonar. The first and more successful of the submarines was the *Nautilus*, which was commissioned in April 1955 with a Westinghouse S2W pressurised water-cooled reactor powering two sets of geared steam turbines delivering some 13,400hp (9,990kW) to two propellers for a submerged speed of 23 knots. The *Seawolf*, which was finally commissioned in March 1957, was less successful as a result of the poor performance of the General Electric S2G liquid sodium-cooled reactor, powering two sets of geared steam turbines delivering some 13,000hp (9,693kW) to two propellers for a submerged speed of about 20 knots.

It was the *Nautilus* and its water-cooled reactor system that paved the way for succeeding generations of American nuclear-powered submarines. It is worth noting here that this pioneering boat retained the type of hull/sail shape

introduced by the 'Type XXI' class although on a somewhat larger scale, as indicated by the submerged displacement of 4,092 tons. This greater size was dictated largely by the volume of the reactor system and its associated shielding, and meant that the boat was not as agile under the surface as its predecessors, but experience soon showed that the extra interior volume provided by the additional cross-section right along the hull was vital to the success of the protracted underwater sortie made possible by the nuclear powerplant. The length of the sortie in a nuclear-powered boat was now limited not by energy and/or air considerations, but rather by the quantity of food that could be carried and by the habitability of the crew accommodation: both of these factors were improved by the greater internal volume now available.

The first nuclear-powered production boats were the four units of the 'Skate' class of attack submarines built between 1955 and 1959. These were

—— The Submarine-Launched Ballistic Missile ——

ABLE to operate as a mobile entity in any area within range of the target, the ballistic missile submarine is a far harder target than any missile-launch site in a fixed location on the Earth's surface, especially as in its definitive form with a nuclear powerplant and submarine- rather than surface-launched missiles such a submarine is independent of the sea's surface for the full length of its patrol. This makes it very difficult for any possible opponent to detect and track such a submarine as it patrols quietly in a very large volume of water. The nature of this submerged patrol made it essential from the beginning of these strategic activities that effective means were found for the submarine to receive messages from its national command authorities, and to know with very great precision its exact geographical location at any moment. The communications capability was provided initially by the release of an antenna lifted to the surface by a small buoy and then by the development of extremely low frequency (ELF) radio waves able to penetrate to the submerged submarine, and the navigational capability was provided by the ship's inertial navigation system (SINS). The latter is an extremely sophisticated equipment into which the ship's position is loaded at the beginning of the patrol: the submarine's three-dimensional movements (in terms of direction and acceleration) are then measured by highly precise gyroscopic systems and integrated with a time function in the SINS's computer to produce a highly accurate plot of the submarine's position, which is required not only for navigation but also for accurate targeting of the missiles. The primary generations of this type of inertially guided missile in American service have been four types designed and built by Lockheed as the UGM-27 Polaris, UGM-73 Poseidon, UGM-96 Trident I and UGM-133 Trident II. The Polaris entered service in 1960 with a warhead yielding 0.5 megatons (later replaced by three 200-kiloton warheads), and in three variants increased in weight from 28,000lb (12,701kg) to 35,000lb (15,876kg) and in length from 28ft 0in (8.53m) to 32ft 3.5in (9.85m) for a range increased from 1,380 miles (2,221km) to 2,880 miles (4,635km). From the 1970s the Polaris was complemented and then replaced by the Poseidon with a warhead bus carrying between 10 and 14 multiple independently targeted re-entry vehicles (MIRVs) each carrying a 40-kiloton warhead delivered with a mean accuracy of 605yds (553m), a weight of 64,000lb (29,030kg), a length of 34ft 0in (10.36m), and a range variable between 2,485 miles (4,000km) increasing to 3,230 miles (5,600km). The Trident I entered service in 1979 after development as a longer-ranged weapon whose availability would increase the size of the deeper-water patrol areas that could be used by American missile submarines. With eight MIRVs each carrying a 100-kiloton warhead delivered with a mean accuracy of 600yds (549m), the Trident I weighs 70,000lb (31,751kg), has a length of 34ft 0in (10.36m), and possesses a range of 4,230 miles (6,808km). The current weapon is the Trident II that entered service in the late 1980s with considerably improved targeting accuracy for its larger number of more powerful warheads. The Trident II thus has a weight of 130,000lb (58,968kg), a length of 44ft 6.6in (13.58m), and a range of 7,500 miles (12,070km) with ten 335-kiloton warheads delivered with an accuracy of 130yds (120m), although a maximum of 15 similar warheads can be fired over a shorter range.

A member of the 'Thresher' (later 'Permit' class) of nuclear-powered attack submarines, the *Whale* here surfaces through the ice of the polar regions, which the essentially unlimited endurance of nuclear propulsion made fully accessible to modern submarines for a significant extension of their operating areas.

smaller boats, similar to the conventionally powered 'Tang' class in overall dimensions, and had a smaller Westinghouse S3W or S4W reactor powering two sets of geared steam turbines delivering 6,600hp (4,921kW) to two propellers for a submerged speed of about 20 knots. The boats had the same BQS-4 sonar, but the armament was increased to eight 21in (533mm) tubes by the addition of two in the stern. The success of the 'Skate' class paved the way for the US Navy's comprehensive move into nuclear propulsion for its submarines, and further development into larger and steadily more capable classes was based on the combination of the nuclear powerplant, in progressively powerful and reliable forms and generally driving a single propeller, with the 'teardrop' hull pioneered by the *Albacore*, and evermore sophisticated computer-assisted sonar systems relying increasingly on the passive mode for the detection and tracking of target submarines, whose

The Wire-Guided Torpedo

WITH the original type of locomotive torpedo based on a gyroscopically controlled unit for guidance, the weapon was committed once it had left its tube with the data (either straight or curved course, depth and speed/range parameters) inputted before launch on the basis of the solution to the fire-control problem worked out in the submarine's control spaces on the basis of variables such as target bearing, course, range and speed (plus anticipated changes in these factors) derived from acoustic and optical observation. Any unexpected changes in the target's data therefore nullified the results of the fire-control calculation. With the development of the wire-guided torpedo, however, the torpedo is launched on the basis of the original fire-control solution but its guidance package can then be provided, throughout its attack, with an updated fire-control solution processed by the submarine's fire-control computer on the basis of changed data. This allows constantly improvement of the fire-control solution, and in the event of a break in the guidance wire link, the torpedo can continue the attack on the basis of the data currently stored in the computer of its guidance package.

Typical of the older submarines maintained in first-line service virtually up to the present is the *Papanikolos* of the Greek navy, a 'GUPPY IIA' conversion of a 'Balao' class fleet submarine dating from World War II.

Designed specifically for the submarine hunter-killer role, the *Rubis* is the lead boat of the French navy's sole nuclear-powered attack submarine class. These eight boats are currently the smallest submarines of their type in operational service.

range is acquired only at the last minute by the active 'ping'.

The first of these new classes was the 'Skipjack' class of six boats with a submerged speed of about 30 knots and an armament of six 21in (533mm) bow tubes for 24 torpedoes, followed by the 'Thresher' (later 'Permit') class of 11 boats with a submerged speed of about 27 knots and an armament of four 21in amidships tubes for 22 Mk 48 wire-guided torpedoes (or 18 torpedoes and four UUM-44 SUBROC underwater-launched rockets each carrying a small homing torpedo as payload) to allow the incorporation of larger and more sophisticated passive/active sonar in the optimum bow position. This class paved the way for the first very large class, which was the 'Sturgeon' class of 42 boats characterised by a sub-merged speed of about 26 knots and an armament of four 21in amidships tubes for 23 Mk 48 torpedoes or 19 torpedoes and four SUBROC weapons.

These boats were completed between 1966 and 1975, and were the mainstay of the US Navy's hunter-killer submarine capability until the later 1970s, when the first of an eventual 62 'Los Angeles' class boats entered service. Completed between 1976 and 1987, these boats each have a submerged displacement in the order of 6,925 tons, a submerged speed of 32 knots on the 35,000hp (26,095kW) supplied to one propeller by the two geared steam turbines powered by one S6G reactor, and an armament of four 21in amidships tubes for a total of 26 weapons, whose versatile fit can include Mk 48 torpedoes, UGM-84 Harpoon submarine-launched anti-ship missiles and BGM-109 Tomahawk cruise missiles in a typical mix of 14, four and eight respectively: the later boats also have vertical launch tubes for 12 Tomahawk missiles, allowing the weapons launched through the amidships tubes to be concentrated on the Mk 48 and Harpoon types, although these can be replaced by up to 78 mines for further expansion of the submarine's operational capabilities.

From the mid-1990s, the 'Los Angeles' class boats are to be supplemented and eventually replaced by the 'Seawolf' class with a submerged displacement of 9,150 tons, a submerged speed of 35 knots driven by a single pumpjet propulsor powered by the 60,000hp (44,735kW) provided by the S6W reactor.

In the period after World War II, the Royal Navy modernised a number of its submarines to conform more closely with the design details that had made the German 'Type XXI' class submarines such a potential threat. This programme included the conversion of 14 'A' class boats, such as the *Alaric* illustrated here, to the 'A (Modernised)' class configuration with a lengthened hull, streamlined forward and after casings, the conning tower replaced by a sail, and the four external torpedo tubes (two in the bows and the other two in the stern) removed to leave a total of six 21in (533mm) tubes in the bows for 18 torpedoes.

The armament of these boats is eight 25.6in (650mm) tubes for a total of about 50 tube-launched weapons or a larger number of mines.

The American lead into nuclear-powered attack submarines was followed with as little delay as possible by the USSR, whose first class of this type was the 'November' class, of which 12 were delivered between 1958 and 1964. The type had a submerged displacement of 5,300 tons, a submerged speed in the order of 30 knots on the 30,000hp (22,370kW) delivered to two propellers by the geared steam turbines powered by a single reactor, and an armament of eight 21in bow tubes for 24 torpedoes. The type was not notably successful because of its high levels of underwater noise, and it also suffered from the unreliability of its nuclear reactor, which was poorly shielded and therefore exercised a distinctly malign influence on its crews.

In 1968 there appeared the first of the succeeding 'Victor' class, which

The *Ethan Allen* was the lead boat of the five-strong class that was the US Navy's first purpose-designed ballistic missile submarine class, and was completed in August 1961 with the flat-topped missile compartment for 16 UGM-27 Polaris missiles, in two longitudinal rows of eight missiles, abaft the sail.

Completed in December 1960, the *Dolfijn* was the lead boat of the Dutch navy's four-strong 'Dolfijn' class of conventionally powered attack submarines with a triple hull arrangement with the three pressure cylinders disposed in a triangular pattern.

Hunter-killer Armament

DESIGNED for the detection and destruction of other boats, the nuclear-powered hunter/killer submarine was initially armed with torpedoes (replaceable by tube-launched mines) for attacks on targets identified and tracked with the aid of increasingly sophisticated sonar of the active and, increasingly, the passive types. The longer range and accuracy of these detection and tracking systems then led to the development of the wire-guided torpedo for long-range engagements. The wire-guided torpedo lacks the range of its launch submarine's sensors, however, and this led to the concept of the submarine-launched rocket, which was an encapsulated weapon fired from an otherwise standard torpedo tubes to reach the surface, break open and release a ballistic rocket that flew to the vicinity of the target and there released into the water either a homing torpedo or a nuclear depth change. Typical weapons of this type include the Honeywell UUM-44 SUBROC introduced to American service in 1965 with a 5 kiloton depth charge delivered over a range of 35 miles (56km), the SS-N-15 'Starfish' introduced to Soviet service in 1972 with a 5 kiloton depth charge delivered over a range of 23 miles (37km), and the SS-N-16 'Stallion' introduced to Soviet service in the mid-1970s with a homing torpedo or nuclear depth charge delivered over a range of 34 miles (55km). From these weapons it was only a short conceptual step to the tube-launched encapsulated anti-ship and cruise missiles (typically the McDonnell Douglas UGM-84 Harpoon and General Dynamics BGM-109 Tomahawk respectively) used by several Western navies to increase the operational versatility of their hunter/killer submarines.

The emergence of a submarine-launched ballistic missile from the water is always a highly impressive sight as the weapon seems to shake itself free of the water, straighten itself, accelerate and then turn onto the desired climb angle. This is a Trident test launch from a submarine of the US Navy.

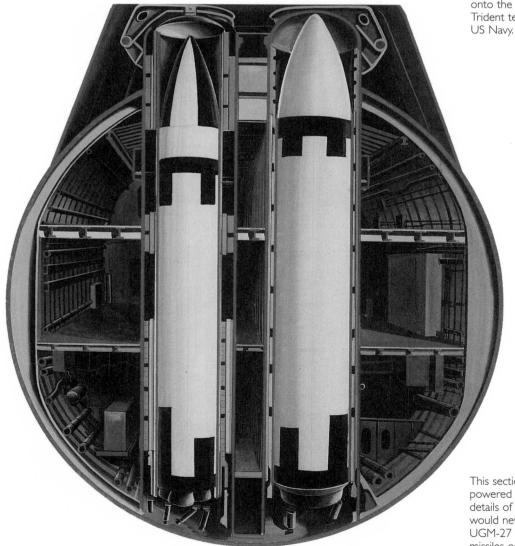

This section through an American nuclear-powered ballistic missile submarine shows details of a side-by-side installation (that would never have been made in reality) of UGM-27 Polaris and UGM-73 Poseidon missiles on the left and right respectively.

This view of part of the interior of the *Repulse*, a 'Resolution' class nuclear-powered ballistic missile submarine of the Royal Navy, reveals the considerably greater volume and efficiency-generating comfort of modern submarines by comparison with the cramped interiors of their diesel-electric predecessors in World War II.

The *Repulse* seen on the surface gives a good impression of the whale-like proportions of modern submarines.

was developed through three main variants in a programme that lasted to 1991 and was the first Soviet submarine with a 'teardrop' hull. The first variant was the 'Victor I' class that was delivered to the extent of 15 submarines up to 1974, with a submerged displacement of 5,300 tons, a submerged speed of 32 knots on the 30,000hp (22,370kW) delivered to one propeller by the geared steam turbine powered by two reactors, and an armament of six 21in bow tubes for either 24 torpedoes or 22 torpedoes and two SS-N-15 'Starfish' anti-ship missiles. There followed the 'Victor II' class of which seven were delivered up to 1978, with a longer hull to provide improved torpedo reload facilities, a submerged displacement of 5,800 tons and a submerged speed of 30 knots. Finally there was the 'Victor III' class of which 26 were delivered up to 1991 to an improved 'Victor II' class design with a submerged displacement of 6,000 tons, a submerged speed of 30 knots, and an armament of two 21in and four 25.6in tubes all in the bows for up to 24 torpedoes, or for a reduced number of torpedoes to allow carriage of SS-N-15 'Starfish' and/or SS-N-16 'Stallion' anti-submarine missiles and SS-N-21 'Samson' cruise missiles.

Whereas these four classes were each based on a nuclear reactor with pressurised water cooling, the following two types switched to a reactor

Lead boat of the Dutch navy's two-strong 'Zwaardvis' class of conventionally powered submarines, the *Zwaardvis* was completed in August 1972 after construction between July 1966 and July 1970 by Rotterdam Dry Dock, and the details of the class include surfaced and submerged displacements of 2,350 and 2,640 tons respectively, a length of 219ft 6in (66.9m), a single-shaft diesel-electric propulsion arrangement with three diesel engines and one 5,000hp (3,728kW) electric motor for surfaced and submerged speeds of 13 and 20 knots respectively, and an armament of six 21in (533mm) tubes in the bows for 20 torpedoes.

cooled by a liquid metal, probably sodium. The first of these was the 'Alfa' class with a hull made of a titanium alloy rather than steel for the extreme diving depth of 2,295ft (700m) and a submerged speed of 45 knots on the 47,000hp (35,045kW) supplied to one propeller by two steam turbo-alternators powered by two reactors. The armament is six 21in bow tubes for 20 weapons including two SS-N-15 'Starfish' anti-submarine missiles.

The six 'Alfa' class boats were built between 1979 and 1983, and were then followed by the first of six 'Sierra' class submarines with a slightly reduced diving depth, a submerged displacement of 8,200 tons, and a submerged speed of about 34 knots on the 40,000hp (29,825kW) supplied to one propeller by two steam turbo-alternators powered by two reactors. The armament is four 21in and four 25.6in tubes for 22 weapons including a

The *Humaita* is one of three 'Oberon' class conventionally powered submarines bought from the UK by the Brazilian navy in the 1970s. The type has surfaced and submerged displacements of 2,030 and 2,410 tons respectively, a length of 295ft 3in (90.0m), a two-shaft diesel-electric propulsion arrangement with 3,680hp (2,745kW) diesel engines and 6,000hp (4,475kW) electric motor for surfaced and submerged speeds of 12 and 17 knots respectively, a crew of 69, and an armament of six 21in (533mm) tubes in the bows for 20 Mk 24 Tigerfish wire-guided torpedoes or 50 mines.

The *Arica*, last of the Peruvian navy's six-strong 'Type 209/1' class of conventionally powered submarines, is seen leaving Kiel after completion by Howaldtswerke in January 1975.

Although planned to a total of 180 units, the Soviet 'Foxtrot' class of conventionally powered submarines was in fact built to the extent of 'only' 62 boats between 1958 and 1971.

The Italian navy's *Leonardo da Vinci* was originally the US Navy's Dace of the 'Gato' class, and was transferred in December 1954 for service up to 1973.

variable number of SS-N-15, SS-N-16 and SS-N-21 missiles. The last type of nuclear-powered attack submarine developed in the USSR and still in very low rate production for the Commonwealth of Independent States is the 'Akula' class with a submerged displacement of 9,100 tons, a submerged speed of 32 knots on the power delivered to one propeller by the steam turbines driven by two pressurised water-cooled reactors; the armament is basically identical to that of the preceding 'Sierra' class.

These Soviet boats do not match the quietness of the American submarines they were built to rival, and also lack the sophistication of the American vessels in their sonar and fire-control systems.

The 'Charlie' class submarine, of which 21 were built for the USSR in three subclasses, was a nuclear-powered type optimised for the carriage and launch of nuclear-armed cruise missiles.

Although China has pretensions to nuclear-powered submarine capability, having produced four or five operational 'Han' class boats, the only other two countries that can genuinely be regarded as members of this exclusive club are the UK and France. The first of the British boats was the *Dreadnought* that was commissioned in 1963 with what was virtually the after end and propulsion arrangement of the American 'Skipjack' class submarine grafted onto a British forward end with British equipment and weapons. The following 'Valiant' class, of which five were built between 1962 and 1971, was a slightly larger and bulkier development incorporating a British reactor system for a submerged displacement of 4,900 tons, a submerged speed of 28 knots on the 15,000hp (11,185kW) supplied to one propeller by a geared steam turbine powered by a pressurised water-cooled reactor, and an armament of six 21in tubes for 26 torpedoes. Further development of the British concept of attack submarines resulted in the 'Swiftsure' and 'Trafalgar' classes. The 'Swiftsure' class, of which six were delivered between 1973 and 1980 with a shorter and fuller hull for increased diving depth, has a submerged displacement of 4,500 tons, a submerged speed of 30 knots, and an armament of five 21in bow tubes for 25 torpedoes or a mix of torpedoes and Harpoon anti-ship missiles. The 'Trafalgar' class, of which seven were delivered from 1983, is a quietened version of the

The *Flasher* was a standard member of the US Navy's 'Sturgeon' class of nuclear-powered attack submarines optimised for the hunter-killer role with considerable underwater speed, advanced BQQ-2 sonar in the optimum bow position, and four 21in (533mm) tubes amidships for wire-guided torpedoes.

The Italian navy's second submarine named *Leonardo da Vinci* is one of the four-strong 'Sauro' class. Built by CRDA in the period between June 1978 and October 1979, the boat was completed in 1981 with details that included surfaced and submerged displacements of 1,456 and 1,641 tons respectively, a length of 209ft 7in (63.9m), a single-shaft diesel-electric propulsion arrangement with 3,210hp (2,394kW) diesel engines and a 3,650hp (2,721kW) electric motor for surfaced and submerged speeds of 12 and 20 knots respectively, a crew of 45, and an armament of six 21in (533mm) tubes in the bows for twelve A184 wire-guided torpedoes. Notable features are the cruciform of control surfaces on the stern, and the large seven-bladed propeller located at the extreme stern.

'Swiftsure' class with an improved reactor and pumpjet propulsion for a submerged speed of 32 knots at a displacement of 5,200 tons.

France has produced only one class of nuclear-powered attack submarine, the eight very small units of the 'Rubis' class delivered from 1983 and still in production. The type has a submerged displacement of 2,670 tons, a submerged speed of 25 knots on the 9,500hp (7,085kW) delivered to one propeller by an electric motor drawing current from two steam turbo-alternators driven by one pressurised water-cooled reactor, and an armament of four 21in tubes for 18 weapons including torpedoes and missiles.

As noted above, the primary attraction of the nuclear propulsion arrangement for underwater craft is that it turns these boats from mere submersibles into true submarines that can operate for very long periods in a fashion wholly independent of the surface. This has allowed nuclear-powered submarines to submerge on leaving base and to surface only when returning to base after a patrol of typically 60 days, and has adversely

Built in larger numbers than any other conventionally powered submarine of Western origins in the period after World War II, the German-designed 'Type 209' offers its potential customers full optimisation for specific roles through the highly adaptable features that permit the completion of the boat to any of several basic sizes with a choice of several weapon and electronic features. Seen left is a view typical of the interior of a 'Type 209' submarine, and below is the *Salta*, one of the Argentine navy's two 'Type 209/1' class boats commissioned in May 1974. A total of 20 such boats has been sold to five countries including Peru and Turkey, whose navies each operate six of the class.

The *Aréthuse* was one of the French navy's four 'Aréthuse' class conventionally powered hunter-killer submarines optimised for operations in the Mediterranean, and was deleted in April 1979.

The *Hyatt* is one of two 'Oberon' class conventionally powered submarines bought from the UK by the Chilean navy.

The *Emily Hobhouse* was one of three 'Daphné' class conventionally powered submarinse bought from France by the South African navy.

The *Amazonas* was one of two 'GUPPY III' class conventionally powered submarines secured from the USA by the Brazilian navy.

The *Tireless* was one of five 'T' class submarines of riveted rather than welded construction that were modified between 1950 and 1956 to the 'T (Streamline)' configuration with all guns removed, the casing streamlined, the conning tower streamlined into a sail, but with no modifications made to the propulsion arrangement. The details of the streamlined class included surfaced and submerged displacements of 1,090 and 1,424 tons respectively, a length of 273ft 6in (83.4m), a tow-shaft propulsion arrangement with 2,500hp (1,864kW) diesel engines and 1,450hp (1,081kW) electric motors for surfaced and submerged speeds of 15.25 and 9.5 knots respectively, a crew of 50, and an armament of six 21in (533mm) tubes for 11 torpedoes. This adapted type was not as effective in operational terms as the 'T (Conversion)' class, but was very useful for anti-submarine warfare training as it was faster and quieter than before. The five boats were all retired and scrapped between 1965 and 1970.

affected the ability of aircraft and surface warships, even when fitted with advanced sonar and magnetic-anomaly detection (MAD), to detect and track such submarines, especially when submarines could achieve unprecedented underwater speeds and were capable of diving to considerable depths. The former resulted in a dramatically increased search area to be covered by aircraft and surface warships, and the latter opened the possibility of using the different salinities and temperatures of greater volumes of water to help degrade the ability of searching sonar systems to acquire and track the submarine.

All these factors combined with development of the ship's inertial navigation system (SINS) and the nuclear-tipped ballistic missile to create one of the ultimate strategic weapons of the present day, namely the submarine-launched ballistic missile submarine that lurks in its patrol area for a long period, ready at command to unleash a devastating salvo of missiles which, as a result of the extremely accurate launch position inputted from the SINS, can be targeted with incredible accuracy. The submarine-launched ballistic missile (SLBM) has three primary advantages over the land-launched equivalent: firstly, its mobile launching point, which renders virtually impossible the chances of any pre-emptive attack by enemy missiles; secondly, its comparatively small size in relation to its land-launched counterpart, a fact made possible by the fact that virtually no point on Earth is more than 1,700 miles (2,735km) from the sea whereas

Left: The *Arashio* was the fifth and last unit of the Japanese navy's 'Oshio' class of conventionally powered submarines, which were the first fleet boats built in Japan after World War II. The submarine was completed in July 1969 after construction by Mitsubishi between July 1967 and October 1968. The details of this class included surfaced and submerged displacements of 1,650 and 2,150 tons respectively, a length of 288ft 8in (61.0m), a two-shaft propulsion arrangement with 2,300hp (1,715kW) diesel engines and 6,300hp (4,697kW) electric motor for surfaced and submerged speeds of 14 and 18 knots respectively, a crew of 80, and an armament of eight 21in (533mm) torpedo tubes located as six in the bows and two in the stern.

Below: The *Nazario Sauro* is the lead boat of the Italian navy's four-strong 'Sauro' class of conventionally powered submarines. Considerable delay in construction was caused by Italian financial problems between the mid-1960s and early 1970s, and then technical problems with the Italian batteries required the purchase of Swedish batteries.

The *Ouessant* was the fourth and last unit of the French navy's 'Agosta' class of conventionally powered submarines delivered in 1977 and 1978 with design emphasis placed not on range but rather on reduced noise, increased diving depth and greater submerged speed.

The *Okanagan* is one of three 'Oberon' class conventionally powered submarines operated by the naval element of the Canadian Armed Forces.

Opposite: The *Renown* is the third of the four 'Resolution' class nuclear-powered submarines that formed the backbone of the UK's strategic deterrent force until the advent of the 'Vanguard' class in the early 1990s.

Le Redoutable is the name boat of the class of nuclear-powered submarines that provides France with its primary nuclear deterrent capability.

Increased Versatility for the Missile Submarine

WITH the exception of China's single such boat, the nuclear-powered ballistic missile submarines placed in service by the world's other major nuclear powers (the USA, USSR, UK and France) were planned within the context of a possible World War III resulting from an armed confrontation between the two superpower blocs. This called for the use of increasingly sophisticated missiles that could penetrate high-grade physical and electronic defences to hit ever increasing numbers of military targets with pinpoint accuracy. When the 'Cold War' between the superpower blocs ended in the late 1980s with the economic and political collapse of the USSR, there were suggestions that the missile submarine was now superfluous. It soon became clear, however, that the world faces a crisis in the proliferation of nuclear weapons capability to countries of doubtful political stability, and with agendas driven as much by tumultuous political and religious antipathies as by rational thought. None of these 'loose pistol' members or would-be members of the nuclear club has a large or even very sophisticated nuclear capability, but all seem more disposed than any of the club's longer-term members to exert 'blackmail' pressure or even to use their weapons. This has given the missile-armed submarine a renewed life, for all of these countries can be watched from space and targeted by submarines with missiles carrying not MIRVed warheads but one or two medium-yield weapons that could be used for the excision of 'loose cannon' nuclear (or for that matter biological and/or chemical) warfare capability should the situation demand.

Opposite top: The *Sjöhästen* is one of the five 'Sjöormen' class conventionally powered attack submarines operated by the Swedish navy. Features of the class include a teardrop-shaped hull, an X-shaped configuration of the control surfaces at the stern, the forward set of hydroplanes located on the sail rather than the forward part of the hull, and a slow-turning five-blade propeller at the extreme stern for the quietest possible operation.

Right: The *Onondaga* is one of three 'Oberon' class submarines operated by the naval branch of the Canadian Armed Forces.

Opposite bottom: The 'Type 207' class of coastal submarine was designed in Germany for Norway on the basis of the 'Type 205' class operated by the German navy, and in the late 1980s Norway transferred three of its boats to Denmark. The basic specification for the class includes surfaced and submerged displacements of 370 and 435 tons respectively, a length of 149ft 0in (45.4m), a single-shaft diesel-electric propulsion arrangement with 1,210hp (900kW) diesel engines and one 1,710hp (1,275kW) electric motor for surfaced and submerged speeds of 12 and 18 knots respectively, a crew of 18, and an armament of eight 21in (533mm) tubes in the bows for eight Tp61 wire-guided anti-ship and NT 37C wire-guided anti-submarine torpedoes. Illustrated here is the Norwegian *Skolpen*, which was commissioned in August 1966 after construction by Rheinstahl. The Danish boats and six of the surviving Norwegian boats have been lengthened to 154ft 3in (47.0m) to allow the incorporation of updated fire-control and navigation electronics.

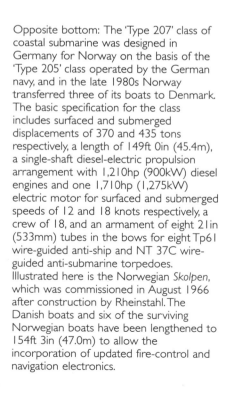

The *Triaina* was a 'Balao' class submarine transferred on loan from the USA to Greece in February 1965 and bought by the Greek navy in April 1976. The boat still existed into the mid-1980s but was confined to alongside training.

land-launched strategic missiles generally have to be launched from considerably greater ranges and must therefore be larger to carry more fuel; and thirdly, that countermeasures against nuclear-powered submarines are made very difficult by reason of the factors mentioned above. It is worth noting, moreover, that while first-generation SLBMs such as the Lockheed UGM-27 Poseidon were indeed comparatively small weapons of the intermediate-range type with a range in the order of 2,750 miles (4,425km) and the ability to carry one warhead, later weapons such as the second-generation Lockheed UGM-73 Poseidon were larger and were capable of a range in the order of 3,250 miles (5,230km) with a payload of 10 or 14 warheads; third-generation weapons such as the Lockheed UGM-96 Trident I were even larger for a range of some 4,250 miles (6,840km) with slightly fewer but independently and more precisely targeted warheads; and fourth-generation weapons such as the Lockheed UGM-133 Trident II are larger still for a range of 7,500 miles (12,070km) with between 10 and 12 independently and more precisely targeted

Still a Case for the Conventionally Powered Submarine

ALTHOUGH the nuclear-powered submarine offers far higher overall capabilities in terms of speed, endurance, weapons load and electronic sophistication in comparison with the conventionally powered submarine, it is also considerably more expensive and, for some specialised applications, not as effective as the conventionally powered boat. The factor of expense, in the development, construction and running of the boats, puts the nuclear-powered submarine out of the running for many navies, most of which do not in any event require the long endurance and deep oceanic capabilities that are the forte of such boats. For these smaller navies, therefore, the conventionally powered submarine provides more than adequate capabilities, especially in the shallower waters typical of coast-defence operations. Here the smaller size of the conventionally powered submarine is a decided asset, as is its propulsion arrangement, which is generally quieter than that of nuclear-powered boats which on a regular basis need to run the pumps associated with their reactor coolant systems. It has to be admitted, of course, that conventionally powered submarines are still not independent of the surface for purposes of refilling their air tanks and charging their batteries, but the submerged endurance of such boats is now significantly better than that of their counterparts in World War II, as a result of the widespread use of snorting and fairly radical improvements in chemical and physical technologies. The disparity between submarines with conventional and nuclear propulsion is being further narrowed, at least in tactical terms, by current developments in fuel cell and closed-cycle engine technologies, both of which offer higher and longer-endurance submerged power as well as the possibility of oxygen as a by-product.

The *Narval* was the last of the four 'S 60' class submarines constructed in Cartagena for the Spanish navy between August 1968 and November 1975 as licence-built versions of the French 'Daphné' class design.

The *Mochishio* is the second of the 10 'Yuushio' class conventionally powered submarines operated by the Japanese navy.

warheads. The Soviets sought to emulate the technological steps that allowed the Americans to develop and build these more advanced weapons, but they never managed to achieve the targeting accuracies of the American weapons, whose longer range meant that the launch submarines could operate in larger patrol areas in the deeper waters farther offshore, thereby reducing the chances of detection and destruction.

The first nuclear-powered ballistic missile submarines were the five units of the 'George Washington' class, which were built for the US Navy in the period between 1957 and 1961. The design was basically that of the 'Skipjack' class nuclear-powered attack submarine with the hull cut in half for the insertion of a constant-section missile compartment, some 130ft

(39.6m) long, immediately to the rear of the sail. This carried 16 vertical container/launcher tubes for the Polaris missile, and the result was a vessel with a submerged displacement of 6,710 tons and a submerged speed of about 20 knots.

The first American SLBM submarines designed as such were the five boats of the 'Ethan Allen' class, which were built between 1959 and 1963 to a design that was equivalent to the 'Thresher' class of attack submarines but with a hull of stronger alloy for the ability to dive deeper, improved quietening features, a towed-array passive sonar for defensive purposes, a submerged displacement of 7,885 tons, a submerged speed of about 20 knots, and a primary armament basically similar to that of the 'George Washington' class, namely 16 Polaris missiles as well as four rather than six 21in torpedo tubes.

Further development resulted in the somewhat larger 'Lafayette' class boat with a submerged displacement of 8,250 tons, a submerged speed of about 25 knots, and an armament of 16 missiles (originally Polaris but later Poseidon weapons) together with four 21in torpedo tubes. Construction of these 19 submarines was undertaken between 1961 and 1964, with the generally similar but quieter 'Benjamin Franklin' class of 12 submarines following between 1963 and 1967. As well as their improved quietening,

The *Splendid* was the last of six 'Swiftsure' class nuclear-powered attack submarines built for the Royal Navy in the period between June 1969 and January 1980 to supplement and then replace the five boats of the older and less capable 'Valiant' class. The design was a development of the 'Valiant' class design with a shorter and fuller hull form for deeper-diving capability and higher submerged speed at the expense of one of the six torpedo tubes carried in the 'Valiant' class.

The Cruise Missile

AFTER a brief flirtation with the submarine-launched cruise missile (the Regulus I and II weapons launched from two conventionally powered and one nuclear-powered submarines) in the late 1950s and early 1960s, the US Navy virtually ignored the cruise missile until the mid-1980s when it adopted conventionally armed versions of the General Dynamics BGM-109 Tomahawk weapon for submarine-launched attacks on ship and land targets, the latter predominating in the extensive use of the weapon as part of the USA's contribution to the UN-led war of 1991 to oust the Iraqi invaders from Kuwait. The USSR, on the other hand, from the mid-1950s devoted considerable attention to the cruise missile for strategic tasks. These tasks fell into two main categories as attacks on major land targets and the destruction of operationally vital maritime targets, most notably the carrier battle groups and amphibious task forces that the USSR saw as a major threat to its survival in the face of supposed American aggression. In order of their appearance in the combined US and NATO terminology for such weapons, these were the SS-N-3 'Shaddock' anti-ship missile with a conventional or 350-kiloton nuclear warhead, the SS-N-7 'Starbright' anti-ship missile with a conventional or 200-kiloton nuclear warhead, the SS-N-9 'Siren' anti-ship missile with a conventional or 200-kiloton nuclear warhead, the SS-N-12 'Sandbox' anti-ship missile with a conventional or 350-kiloton nuclear warhead, the SS-N-19 'Shipwreck' anti-ship missile with a 500-kiloton nuclear warhead, the SS-N-21 'Samson' dual-purpose weapon with a conventional or 250/350-kiloton nuclear warhead, and the SS-N-24 dual-purpose weapon with a conventional or nuclear warhead. Most of these weapons use inertial guidance (with the possibility of mid-course command update) for the mid-course phase of their flights in conjunction with some type of terminal guidance (active radar, passive radar or infra-red) for better accuracy in the attack phase of the flight. Weapons with a nuclear warhead do not need as accurate a terminal-guidance package as the versions with a conventional warhead.

Completed between 1961 and 1968 at Gorky, the 15 nuclear-powered submarines of the 'Juliett' class were designed for the interception and destruction of US Navy carrier battle groups with the aid of a primary armament of four large nuclear-tipped cruise missiles that can be launched only after the submarine has surfaced. These comprise either the SS-N-3C 'Shaddock' with active radar or infra-red terminal guidance for the delivery of a 350 kiloton nuclear or 2,205lb (1,000kg) warhead over a range of 290 miles (467km), or the SS-N-12 'Sandbox' with active radar terminal guidance for the delivery of a 350 kiloton nuclear or 2,205lb (1,000kg) conventional warhead over a range of 345 miles (555km). The missiles are accommodated in two side-by-side pairs of elevating launchers located ahead and abaft of the small sail with distinctive blast deflectors to channel the exhaust gases upward and outward when the missiles are launched at an elevation of about 20 degrees.

these boats introduced a number of detail improvements, and from the late 1970s were revised to carry the Trident I missile in place of the Poseidon.

The last word in SLBM submarines of Western origins is the current mainstay of the US Navy, the altogether larger and more formidable 'Ohio' class of boats, of which 18 are in the process of being commissioned with the main missile battery increased to 24 weapons of the Trident I type in the first eight submarines and the improved Trident II in the remaining 10 submarines. The size of the missile section is so much greater than those of the preceding classes that the overall dimensions and displacement of the 'Ohio' class are increased dramatically: whereas the 'Lafayette' and 'Benjamin Franklin' classes were based on a hull 425ft (129.5m) long with a beam of 33ft (10.05m) and a draught of 31ft 6in (9.6m) for a submerged displacement of 8,250 tons, the 'Ohio' class submarine is based on a hull 560ft (170.7m) long with a beam of 42ft (12.8m) and a draught of 36ft 5in

(11.1m) for a submerged displacement of 18,750 tons. The greater size and displacement of the 'Ohio' class meant that a more powerful propulsion arrangement had to be incorporated lest the performance of the submarine fell to unacceptably low levels: the 'Lafayette' and 'Benjamin Franklin' classes had been based on the use of a single propeller receiving 15,000hp (11,185kW) from the two geared turbines powered by steam from a single Westinghouse S5W reactor for a submerged speed of about 25 knots, but in the 'Ohio' class the single propeller receives 60,000hp (44,736kW) from the two geared steam turbines powered by steam from a single General Electric S8G reactor for a submerged speed of 30 knots. Like its predecessors, the 'Ohio' class submarine also carries torpedo armament in the form of four 21in tubes in the bows for Mk 48 wire-guided torpedoes.

Compared with the Americans, who opted for exclusive use of the ballistic missile for its strategic purposes after a brief flirtation with the winged cruise missile that ended with the one-off Halibut nuclear-powered boat completed in 1960 with a primary armament of two Regulus

The 'Oscar' class submarine of the Soviet navy was designed for the strategic cruise missile role with a very large hull to allow the incorporation of container-launchers four 24 SS-N-19 'Shipwreck' long-range anti-ship missiles.

Below: Built to a Danish design and here epitomised by the lead submarine, the four 'Delfinen' class coastal submarines were built between July 1954 and October 1964 by the Copenhagen Naval Dockyard, with surfaced and submerged displacements of 595 and 643 tons, a length of 178ft 10in (54.5m), a two-shaft propulsion arrangement with 1,200hp (805kW) diesel engines and 1,200hp (895kW) electric motors for surfaced and submerged speeds each of 15 knots, a crew of 33, and an armament of four 21in (533mm) torpedo tubes in the bows.

Built to the extent of six boats produced by Kockums and Karlskrona Navy Yard between 1957 and November 1962, and here epitomised by the *Gripen*, the 'Draken' class was basically an improved version of the 'Hajen' class with one large propeller for reduced noise and improved submerged speed.

Built from December 1976 by Kawasaki and Mitsubishi, the Japanese submarines of the 'Yuushio' class were built to an improved 'Uzushio' class design with deeper-diving capability and more advanced electronics.

Above: The *Pijao* is one of two 'Type
209/1' or 'Type 1200' class conventionally
powered submarines operated by the
Colombian navy with German and Dutch
electronics together with an armament of
German torpedoes.

The *Cakra* is one of two 'Type 209/2' or
'Type 1300' class conventionally powered
submarines operated by the Indonesian
navy with German, French and Dutch
electronics together with an armament of
German torpedoes.

Above: The Japanese 'Uzushio' class is notable for its teardrop-shaped hull and generally good streamlining.

The Western designation 'Zulu IV' was allocated to the class of Soviet conventionally powered submarines adapted from the original 'Zulu I', 'Zulu II' and 'Zulu III' subclasses without any deck gun or similar exterior impediment.

The 'Sauro' class of four boats, here epitomised by the *Nazario Sauro*, was built between June 1974 and September 1982 by Italcantieri to a design optimised for sea-going operations along the whole length of the Mediterranean. The details of the class include surfaced and submerged displacements of 1,455 and 1,630 tons respectively, a length of 210ft 0in (63.9m), a single-shaft diesel-electric propulsion arrangement with 3,645hp (2,718kW) diesel engine and one 3,220hp (2,400kW) electric motor for surfaced, snorting and submerged speeds of 11, 12 and 20 knots respectively, the capability to dive to a maximum of 1,345ft (410m) although 820ft (250m) is the operational limit, a crew of 45 with provision for four trainees, and an armament of six 21in (533mm) tubes in the bows for twelve A 184 wire-guided torpedoes.

Built as cruise missile submarines, the 'Echo II' class of nuclear-powered submarines was originally armed with container-launchers for SS-N-3 'Shaddock' missiles that were replaced in 10 or more boats by the same number of container-launchers for SS-N-12 'Sandbox' missiles.

Opposite: The *Georgia* is the fourth unit of the US Navy's extremely capable 'Ohio' class. The markings on the upper part of the forward hull section are aiming marks so that a rescue submarine can find the docking port in the event of an underwater accident.

Below: Lead boat of the US Navy's largest ballistic missile submarine type, the *Ohio* is exceeded in size only by the boats of the Soviet (now Russian) 'Typhoon' class and carries vertical launch tubes for 24 Trident I missiles.

II or five Regulus I missiles, the Soviets opted for a two-handed approach that saw the development of both conventionally powered and nuclear-powered submarines for the carriage of ballistic missiles for the strategic role, and winged cruise missiles for the strategic role and also for the operational-level role of tracking the American carrier battle groups whose nuclear-armed aircraft were seen as another major threat to the survival of the USSR.

The first of the cruise missile types were the conventionally powered 'Whiskey Long Bin', conventionally powered 'Juliett' and nuclear-powered 'Echo I' classes. The first comprised a number of 'Whiskey' class boats converted between 1961 and 1963 with four SS-N-3 'Shaddock' anti-ship missiles in a process that reduced the type's submerged speed to 8 knots; the second totalled 16 boats built between 1961 and 1969 with four SS-N-3 or later four SS-N-12 missiles and a submerged displacement of 3,750 tons and

Above: This photograph shows the *Ohio* under way on the surface, the size of the submarine and its immense power being readily evident from its considerable bow wave and turbulent wake.

Above: The missile tube covers are clearly visible in this photograph of the *Yankee II*. The object on the large mast at the after end of the fin is an aerial for electronic warfare. Satellite navigation equipment is contained in the large sphere at the forward end.

Left: The massive section immediately abaft the sail on the 'Ohio' class ballistic missile submarine is occupied by the two longitudinal rows each of 12 tubes for the primary armament, which comprises 24 Trident I missiles in the first eight boats and 24 considerably more powerful and accurate Trident II missiles in the last nine boats.

a submerged speed of 14 knots; and the third amounted to five boats built between 1960 and 1962 with an armament of eight SS-N-3 missiles, a submerged displacement of 5,500 tons, and a submerged speed of 25 knots with two propellers receiving 25,000hp (18,640kW) from two sets of geared steam turbines powered by a single reactor. Between 1962 and 1967 there followed 29 'Echo II' class boats with an enlarged sail carrying the type of radar that could provide mid-course guidance updates for the eight SS-N-3 missiles, and with a submerged displacement of 6,000 tons the boats could achieve a submerged speed of 23 knots on basically the same propulsion arrangement as the 'Echo I' class boats.

The primary limitation of the 'Echo' class boats was that they had to surface to fire their missiles, and this tactical limitation was addressed in the following 'Charlie' class of 21 boats delivered between 1968 and 1980 in three subvariants, each armed with eight underwater-launched anti-ship missiles: in the 10 units of the 'Charlie I' class these are SS-N-7 'Starbright' weapons, in the six units of the 'Charlie II' class they are SS-N-9 'Siren' weapons, and in the five units of the 'Charlie III' class they are SS-N-22 'Sunburn' weapons. The 'Charlie I' class has a submerged displacement of 5,000 tons and a submerged speed of 27 knots, while the longer 'Charlie II' and 'Charlie III' classes each have a submerged displacement of 5,500 tons and a submerged speed of 26 knots, in each case with 15,100hp (11,260kW) delivered to one propeller from a set of geared steam turbines powered by a single pressurised water-cooled reactor.

The last of the Soviet cruise missile submarines was the six-strong

Numerically the most important nuclear-powered ballistic missile submarine class in Soviet (now Russian) service, the 'Delta IV' class carries a primary armament of 16 vertically launched SS-N-18 'Stingray' missiles. This has liquid propellants and carries a MIRVed warhead system (with three or seven 200-kiloton warheads as an alternative to one 450-kiloton warhead) by comparison with the solid propellants and non-MIRVed warhead system (one 1.2-megaton or two 800-kiloton warheads) of the SS-N-8 'Sawfly' carried by the preceding 'Delta I' and 'Delta II' classes. The greater length of the SS-N-8 is reflected in the fact that the after casing of the 'Delta III' rises 29ft 6in (9.0m) above the waterline whereas in the two earlier subclasses it was 'only' 25ft 5in (7.75m) above the water.

Built to the extent of only one boat that was lost in 1989, the 'Mike' class design of nuclear-powered attack submarine had a titanium-reinforced hull for a considerable deep-diving capability, and is thought to have used explosive charges rather than compressed air to blow the main ballast tanks at the extremely high pressures encountered at great depths.

'Oscar' class of very large boats built in two subclasses as two 'Oscar I' and four 'Oscar II' class boats, each with a primary armament of 12 two-round launchers for SS-N-19 'Shipwreck' missiles. The 'Oscar I' class has a submerged displacement of 12,500 tons and a submerged speed of 30 knots on the 90,000hp (67,105kW) delivered to two propellers by geared steam turbines powered by two pressurised water-cooled reactors, while the 'Oscar II' class has a submerged speed of 28 knots on the same propulsion arrangement and incorporates improved quietening features that have increased the submerged displacement to 13,400 tons.

Now deleted from service, the *Lafayette* was the lead boat of an extremely important class of nuclear-powered ballistic missile submarines that, with the basically very similar 'Benjamin Franklin' class boats, bore the brunt of the USA's naval deterrent capability between the mid-1960s and mid-1980s.

The *Tireless* is the third unit of the seven-strong 'Trafalgar' class that is the Royal Navy's newest nuclear-powered attack submarine class, all built by Vickers. The class is designed to complement the 'Swiftsure' class, and is notable for its extremely low radiated noise levels resulting largely from the use of a wraparound coating of anechoic tiles and reliance on a pumpjet propulsor rather than a propeller.

Opposite top: Seen with two deep-submergence rescue vehicles (DSRVs) in wells on the after casing, the 'India' class submarine was designed for the rescue role. Only two of the submarines were built, single boats operating with the Soviet (now Russian) Pacific and Northern Fleets, which are the main operators of the deep-ocean submarines that might need the aid of the DSRVs.

Right: The 'Golf II' class has now disappeared from service, although two 'Golf I' class boats remained in service into the early 1990s as command and communications submarines.

Below: Commissioned in January 1983 after construction between September 1979 and April 1981 by the Electric Boat Division of the General Dynamics Corporation, the *City of Corpus Christi* was the eighteenth unit of the 'Los Angeles' class, eventually to number 62 boats as the largest class of nuclear-powered submarines yet envisaged.

After development and initial deployment of ballistic missiles in the conventionally powered 'Golf' class, of which 22 were completed between 1958 and 1962 with a primary armament of three SS-N-4 or later SS-N-5 missiles, both of which had to be launched on the surface, the USSR moved into the field of nuclear-powered ballistic missile submarines with the 'Hotel' class, of which eight were completed between 1958 and 1962 with a primary armament of three SS-N-4 missiles, a submerged displacement of 6,000 tons, and a submerged speed of 26 knots on the 30,000hp (22,370kW) delivered to two propellers by geared steam turbines driven by two pressurised water-cooled reactors. Between 1963 and 1970 the boats were modified to the more capable 'Hotel II' standard with the primary armament revised to three SS-N-5 'Sark' missiles that could be launched while the boats were still submerged.

Although these boats provided an operational capability of types, the first genuine SLBM capability was attained by the USSR with the 34 'Yankee' class submarines delivered between 1963 and 1972, with a submerged displacement of 9,600 tons, a submerged speed of 27 knots on the 50,000hp (37,280kW) delivered to two propellers by geared steam turbines powered by two pressurised water-cooled reactors. The primary armament of these boats was 16 underwater-launched SS-N-6 'Serb' missiles, which may be regarded as having been roughly equivalent to the Polaris weapon used by the US Navy, thus making the 'Yankee' class the Soviet counterpart of the 'Lafayette' class, although the Soviet boats were significantly more noisy and, with a 30 per cent larger propulsion section and 30 per cent smaller missile section, were generally less efficient than their American rivals.

The next series of Soviet SLBM submarines comprised the four subvariants of the 'Delta' class. Built between 1972 and 1977, the 18 'Yankee I' class boats had a submerged displacement of 10,200 tons and a submerged speed of 26 knots on the 50,000hp (37,280kW) delivered to two propellers by the geared steam turbines powered by two pressurised water-cooled reactors, and carried a primary armament of 12 SS-N-8 'Sawfly' underwater-launched missiles. The four 'Delta II' class boats that followed in 1974 and 1975 were lengthened to allow the carriage of 16 rather than 12 missile launch tubes, and with the submerged displacement increased to 11,300 tons, had a submerged speed of 25 knots with the same propulsion arrangement. Next came 14 'Delta III' class boats built between 1974 and 1982, with a slightly longer hull and revisions to carry 16 SS-N-18 'Stingray' missiles with liquid rather than solid propellants, a submerged displacement of 11,700 tons and a submerged speed of 24 knots with an unchanged propulsion arrangement. Finally, there were the six submarines of the 'Yankee IV' class delivered from 1984 as a development of the 'Yankee III' class with the SS-N-23 'Skiff' missile, which is a moderately advanced weapon combining the range of the SS-N-8 with the multiple independently targeted warhead capability of the SS-N-18. The 'Yankee IV' class carries 16 of these weapons, with a submerged displacement of 12,150 tons has a submerged speed of 23.5 knots with an unchanged propulsion arrangement.

The final class of SLBM submarines designed in the USSR is the 'Typhoon' class, which is the largest submarine yet designed and built, with a submerged displacement of 26,500 tons, a submerged speed of 27 knots on the 80,000hp (59,650kW) delivered to two propellers by the geared steam turbines powered by two pressurised water-cooled reactors, and a primary armament of 20 SS-N-20 'Sturgeon' missiles each carrying up to nine independently targeted warheads. Six of the boats have been delivered since 1982. The three other countries that have built nuclear-powered SLBM submarines are China, France and the UK. China's current strength is just one 'Xia' class submarine with a submerged displacement of

Opposite: The largest submarine type yet planned and built, the Soviet (now Russian) 'Typhoon' class boat carries a primary armament of 20 SS-N-10 'Sturgeon' vertically launched ballistic missiles in missile compartments located forward of the sail, and is in essence two pressure hulls and nuclear propulsion plants located side-by-side and connected by a free-flooding outer hull.

Left: The 'Victor' class was built in three subclasses totalling some 48 nuclear-powered boats to provide the Soviet (now Russian) navy with its most important attack submarine type.

8,000tons, a submerged speed of 22 knots, and a primary armament of 12 CSS-N-3 missiles.

France has developed and built three classes of SLBM submarine in the form of the five-strong 'Le Redoutable' class delivered between 1974 and 1980, with a submerged displacement of 8,940 tons, a submerged speed of 25 knots, and a primary armament of 16 M20 or, in one boat, M4 missiles; the single 'L'Inflexible' class submarine developed from the 'Le Redoutable' class with 16 M4 (later M45) missiles; and the planned six units of the 'Le Triomphant' class entering service in the second half of the 1990s with a submerged displacement of 14,335 tons, a submerged speed of 25 knots, and a primary armament of 16 M45 missiles.

Finally there is the UK, which entered the field of the SLBM submarinein 1967 with the commissioning of the first of four 'Resolution' class submarines with a submerged displacement of 8,400 tons, a submerged speed of 25 knots, and a primary armament of 16 Poseidon missiles. From the mid-1990s these are being replaced by the four submarines of the 'Vanguard' class with a submerged speed of 25 knots and a primary armament of 16 Trident II missiles.

With the ending of the confrontation between the two superpower blocs in the late 1980s, the rationale behind the construction and operation of nuclear-powered ballistic missile submarines has been weakened considerably, and it is probable that boats of this type will now be kept in lengthy service with improvements introduced in the form of better equipment and updated versions of the current generation of missiles. The flexibility offered by attack and patrol submarines of the nuclear-powered and conventionally powered types is now more important than ever, however, and it is possible that this will result in continued development of these types.

Glossary

ASDIC   original type of equipment, otherwise known as Asdic, for the detection of submerged targets by acoustic means, and then in improved versions the gathering of data about their bearing and range from the listener

BALLAST   in submarine terms, water that is admitted into the outer part of the hull to replace buoyancy air and thus cause the boat to submerge until the time that the command to surface is givem, whereupon vents at the tops of the ballast tanks are closed and compressed air is released into the tanks, expelling the water and giving the boat positive buoyancy

BALLISTIC MISSILE   missile that flies a ballistic trajectory after motor burn-out

BUNKERAGE   volume for the carriage of the submarine's fuel oil

CASING   external flat decking and its support structure added above the pressure hull on older submarines to provide a flooring for crew movement outside the pressure hull for the purposes of manning the deck gun, revictualling and rearming the boat, and mooring and unmooring the submarine

CONNING TOWER   raised structure carrying the bridge of the submarine above the pressure hull and also accommodating the periscope(s) and any other such extending/raisable unit

CRUISE MISSILE   winged missile that flies an aerodynamic trajectory

DEPTH CHARGE   anti-submarine weapon comprising a large high esxplosive charge packed into a cylindrical steel container and initiated at a pre-set depth (or rather pre-set pressure of water) by a hydrostatic pistol

DIESEL ENGINE   type of internal combustion engine operating on the basis on compression ignition of heavy oil rather than the spark ignition of light petroleum, and therefore better suited to submarine propulsion for its lack of highly volatile petroleum gases as well as its considerably greater operating economy

DIESEL-ELECTRIC   type of propulsion arrangement in which the diesel engines are not geared to the propeller shafts but instead drive electric generators that supply current to the electric motor(s) powering the propeller shaft(s)

'HEDGEHOG'   weapon throwing a pattern of small impact-fused bombs into the water ahead of an attacking warship with the target submarine still located in the Asdic (sonar) beam

HYDROPLANE   horizontal control surface, normally installed as two sets of surfaces near the bows and stern, to control the submarine's attitude in the water

'LIMBO'   trainable weapon throwing a pattern of large depth-fused bombs into the water ahead and/or to the side of an attacking warship with the target submarine still located in Asdic (sonar) beam

MIRV   this Multiple Independently targeted Re-entry Vehicle warhead comprises a bus carrying several warheads that are independently targeted on individual targets after re-entry

MRV   this Multiple Re-entry Vehicle warhead comprises a bus carrying several warheads that are scattered around the target area after re-entry into the atmosphere

PERISCOPE   primary external vision device of a submarine comprising a tall vertical tube containing two inward-facing mirrors angled at 45 degrees to transmit the image gathered by the horizontal lens at the head of the periscope to the eyepiece used by the operator

PRESSURE HULL   basically cylindrical structure bearing the main compression loads as the submarine dives

SAIL   modern version of the conning tower with a more streamlined outer shell and usually containing part of the control space

SNORKEL   mast-mounted device, originally known to the Germans as the *Schnorchel* and the British as the snort, allowing air to be drawn into a submarine just under the surface of the water for the purposes of running the diesel engines for a higher submerged speed and also for recharging of the batteries

SONAR   American name, now universal, for Asdic

'SQUID'   weapon throwing a pattern of large depth-fused bombs into the water ahead of an attacking warship with the target submarine still located in the Asdic (sonar) beam

TORPEDO   in submarine terms, two types of offensive weapon in the forms of the 'spar torpedo' that was a large explosive charge extended over the bows of the boat on a long spar, and the 'locomotive torpedo' that is a self-propelled weapon of basically cylindrical form containing a gyroscopic control mechanism, rear-mounted stabilising fins with attached control surfaces, a propulsion system, a large warhead and, in more modern torpedoes, either a homing system or an external wire-guidance package

Index

Index of boat names